W9-BXB-608

BEHAVIORAL OBJECTIVES

A GUIDE TO INDIVIDUALIZING LEARNING

SCIENCE

JOHN C. FLANAGAN
ROBERT F. MAGER
WILLIAM M. SHANNER

Westinghouse Learning Press
Palo Alto, California
Division of Westinghouse Learning Corporation

Library of Congress Catalog Card Number: 75–149050

First Edition

Printed in the United States of America

CONTENTS

Preface

A huge advantage of an instructional objective derives from the simple fact that it is written. Once it is written, it is visible. Once it is visible, it can be reviewed, evaluated, modified, and improved.

Objectives are frequently discussed but seldom seen. In these volumes you can see approximately four thousand instructional objectives in the subject areas of language arts, mathematics, science, and social studies ranging from grade one through grade twelve. This collection represents the cooperative efforts of over one hundred classroom teachers and an almost equal number of staff members at the American Institute for Research and Westinghouse Learning Corporation.

Since these volumes present written objectives rather than a discussion about objectives, they become the criteria by which materials are selected, content outlined, instructional procedures and educational technology developed, and tests and examinations prepared. All these aspects of an educational program are really the means for accomplishing the basic educational purpose.

This collection serves to stimulate teachers and educators in selecting and developing behavioral objectives for their own use. These objectives may be criticized and evaluated, revised and modified; objectives may be added or deleted, all with the purpose of arriving at an appropriate set of educational outcomes to meet the educational needs of a local situation and of individual students.

The rather obvious purpose of an instructional objective should be to make clear to teachers, students, and other interested persons what youngsters should be able to do as a result of the instructional program. A well-written instructional objective should specify under what conditions and to what extent a certain kind of student performance can be expected.

Unfortunately, school systems commonly lack a comprehensive and reasonably consistent set of educational objectives. Educational goals and objectives are frequently expressed only in broad, global terms, and the question of what and how to teach is left to a considerable extent to the teacher. As a result, quality in the

PREFACE

schools is closely associated with the qualified and skillful teacher. No doubt considerable excellent educational work is done by artistic teachers who, while they may not have a clear conception of goals, do have an intuitive sense of good teaching. Their materials are significant, and they develop topics effectively with students. They clarify the educational objectives (even objectives not directly stated) through their actions as they teach intuitively.

If the foregoing were to serve as a basis for defining education, then the "intuitiveness of the artistic teacher" would have to be built into the educational program. This, of course, cannot be done. The alternative is to start with clearly defined, rather than implied, instructional objectives.

Educational objectives—even clearly stated, specific objectives —are, in the final analysis, matters of choice and thus are value judgments. The question then arises:

> Who provides these value judgments? In the last analysis, the public schools are operated to meet the needs of society. Some of the objectives, along with rules regarding who shall attend school, are provided for in state constitutions and by-laws. Other objectives are set forth by the efforts of elected representatives of the people of a community. Some are provided by professional educators hired to operate the schools. Still others come from our knowledge of children themselves and how they learn. All of these sources effectively furnish the educational objectives for a local public school. Objectives will change with the changing conditions of the times, sometimes quickly, as with Sputnik, but usually slowly.

In evaluating and summarizing instructional objectives, whatever their source, certain kinds of information and knowledge provide a more intelligent basis than others for making decisions about objectives. If certain facts are known and understood, the probability is increased that judgments about objectives will be wise and that educational goals will gain in significance, objectivity, and validity. For this reason the so-called scientific study of the curriculum has largely concerned itself with investigations that may provide a more adequate basis for wise selection of instructional objectives than has previously been available.

What sources can be used for acquiring information from which objectives can be derived? This question has been the subject of much controversy between essentialists and progressives, between

PREFACE

subject specialists and child psychologists, between sociologists and philosophers, between this school group and that school group.

Progressives and child psychologists emphasize the importance of studying the child to find out what kinds of interests he has, what problems he encounters, what purposes he has in mind. They see this information as providing the basic source for selecting objectives. Essentialists and subject specialists, on the other hand, are impressed by the large body of knowledge collected over many thousands of years, the so-called cultural heritage, and emphasize this body of knowledge as the primary source for deriving objectives. They view objectives as essentially the basic learnings selected from the vast cultural heritage of the past.

Many sociologists and others concerned with the pressing problems of contemporary society see in an analysis of today's world the basic information from which objectives can be derived. They view the school as the agency for helping young people to deal effectively with the critical problems of life in modern society. If existing problems can be determined, then, the sociologist feels, the objectives of the school are to provide the knowledge, skills, and attitudes that will help people to deal intelligently and effectively with contemporary problems. On the other hand, educational philosophers recognize that there are basic values in life, largely transmitted from one generation to another by means of education. They see the school as aiming essentially at the transmission of basic values derived by comprehensive philosophic study; hence they view educational philosophy as the source from which objectives can be derived.

The point of view recommended here is that no single source of information is adequate as a basis for wise and comprehensive decisions about the objectives of education. Each of the sources described has certain values to commend it. Each source should be given consideration in planning. In this way educational programs may be developed that are flexible and suitable for any specific public-school situation, regardless of whether that situation is influenced primarily by a single viewpoint or by a combination of attitudes concerning educational objectives.

Although the objectives in these volumes contribute to solving the difficult problem of delineating a curriculum, they should not be considered as a final and perfect product. Any set of objectives must in fact be considered tentative, requiring continuous updating

PREFACE

and reevaluation to the educational purposes and programs at hand. To have critical comments made about one's objectives should be taken as a compliment, since criticism can only be made when one has given the thought and taken the time to write the objectives down.

In spite of the great effort and the number of man-hours that have gone into the task of compiling the objectives in these volumes, several of the objectives listed cannot yet be considered to be "true objectives," if by objectives we mean instructional outcomes described in terms of performance. In fact, the editors wish to make the following comments as to why some of the objectives herein are open to multiple interpretation.

1. Some objectives describe a classroom activity taking place during the process of learning, rather than the performance to be exhibited by the proficient student after learning.

2. Some objectives lack a description of, or even a suggestion for, the stimulus conditions under which a student is to perform. Conversely (and perversely), seemingly unimportant stimulus conditions are occasionally included.

3. Some statements (this term seems more appropriate here than objectives) fail to suggest any sort of criteria. Though not all objectives demand criteria, this lack makes for a certain vagueness in the phrasing of some objectives.

With slight editorial and organizational modifications, the objectives in these volumes are the objectives for Project PLAN. Project PLAN is a system of individualized education, operative at grades one through twelve in the subject areas of language arts, mathematics, science and social studies.

Project PLAN was conceived by Dr. John C. Flanagan, and to some extent evolved from the findings of Project TALENT, a large-scale, long-range project involving the collection of comprehensive information about education in the United States. Project TALENT involved the testing of a sample of 440,000 students in 1,353 secondary schools in all parts of the country in March 1960, with subsequent follow-up studies.

PREFACE

Through Dr. Flanagan's efforts, Project PLAN was brought into being in February 1967 as a joint effort of the American Institute for Research, Westinghouse Learning Corporation, and thirteen school districts.[1] Dr. Flanagan has continued to direct the developmental and research work on Project PLAN since that date. Assisting in the developmental work of Project PLAN has been Dr. Robert F. Mager, who is well known for his book *Preparing Instructional Objectives.*[2] Dr. Mager's philosophy was followed in the development of the objectives in these volumes.

The objectives in these volumes, then, have originated from teachers and have been tried out in schools. We wish to acknowledge the efforts of the teachers (their names are listed below) who were assigned by their school districts to work for a year at the American Institute for Research in Palo Alto. Without their contributions these volumes of objectives would not have been possible.

Archdiocese of San Francisco, Department of Education: Sister Maura Cole, Marian Bonnet, Janice Edminster, Sister Charlene Foster, Sister Bernice Heinz, Sister Patricia Hoffman, Sister Mary Vincent Gularte, Sister Anita Kelly, Sister Jeanne Marie Sosic

---

1. Archdiocese of San Francisco, Department of Education, San Francisco, California; Fremont Unified School District, Fremont, California; San Carlos Elementary School District, San Carlos, California; San Jose Unified School District, San Jose, California; Santa Clara Unified School District, Santa Clara, California; Sequoia Union High School District, Redwood City, California; Union Elementary School District, San Jose, California; Bethel Park School District, Bethel Park, Pennsylvania; Hicksville Public School District, Hicksville, New York; Penn Trafford School District, Harrison City, Pennsylvania; Pittsburgh Public Schools, Pittsburgh, Pennsylvania; Quincy Public Schools, Quincy, Massachusetts; Wood County Schools, Parkersburg, West Virginia.
2. R. F. Mager, *Preparing Instructional Objectives* (Palo Alto, Calif.: Fearon Publishers, 1962). The cooperating school districts furnished classroom teachers each year from 1967 through June 1970 to develop the objectives and to prepare the Teaching-Learning Units that enable students to accomplish the objectives. These teachers worked under the supervision of American Institute for Research and Westinghouse Learning Corporation professional personnel. The director of these activities was Dr. William M. Shanner. At the end of each year the teachers returned to their respective school districts to initiate the instructional programs organized from the objectives.

PREFACE

Bethel Park School District: Lora Moroni, Gordon Lepri, James Johnson, Judith Andrews, Flora Belle Faddis, David Loadman, Mary Lou Ertman, Roger Johnson, Robert N. Manson, Anna Marie Kerlin, Frances Chase, Robert M. Caldwell

Fremont Unified School District: Lyndall Sargent, Gail Pagan, Rex W. Estes, Caroline Breedlove, Monique Lowy, Charles Swanson, Eileen Trefz, Robert Fairlee, Beverly Ulbricht, Forrest W. Dobbs, Roy C. Fields, Bertram K. Robarts

Hicksville Public School District: Elayne Kabakoff, Richard C. Leuci, Terrence Boylan, Janet Findlay, Willard Prince, Edward Albert, Phyllis A. Kabakoff, Lawrence Dauch, Gerald Shanley, Marjorie Giannelli, Tom Bannan, Gerard F. Irwin

Hughson Union High School District: Warren Green

Penn-Trafford School District: Gary Fresch, Mary Ann Kovaly, Michael Demko, Jack Reilly, Victor Bohince, David Garvin, La-Velle Hirshberg, R. Bruce Robinson

Pittsburgh Public Schools: Ann Mulroy, Jean Brooke, Kenneth Fraser, Shirley Fullerton, Ruth Aaron, Donald Coudriet, Cecilia Sukits, Carmen Violi, Samuel D. Martin, Paul J. Schafer, Mary South, Patricia Sellars

Quincy Public Schools: Jean Ann MacLean, Priscilla A. Dauphinee, Francis Keegan, Katherine Norris, Dennis Carini, Richard Russell, Stephen Fishman, Jack K. Merrill, Marcia A. Mitchell, Robert J. Mattsson, Margaret E. Flynn

San Carlos Elementary School District: Helen Dodds, Natalie Klock, Edith Bryant, Maxine Ross, Elizabeth Movinski, Martha A. Elmore, Charles B. Whitlock, Betty Lee, Lee G. Jensen

San Jose Unified School District: Allaire Bryant, Rise Berry, Hal Garrett, Kathy Roberts, William Harvel, Judy Opfer, Judi Wells, Don Crowell, Oran T. Adams, Marilyn D. Johnson, Alice S. Anderson, Sylvia Atallah

Santa Clara Unified School District: Nancy Wylde, Ruth Hessenflow, Arthur A. Hiatt, Herman Neufeld

PREFACE

Sequoia Union High School District: Gale Randall, Rex Fortune, Robert W. DuBois

Union School District: Jo Ann Risko, Peggy Schwartz, Rose Yamasaki, Glenn Moseley, Sue Coffin, Tod Hodgdon, Barbara S. Donley, Frank Kelly

Wood County Schools: Roberta Adkins, Mary Rector, Larry Myers, Virginia Haller, John Hoyes, Connie Chapman, Ada Ardelia Price, David V. Westfall, Nancy M. Rice, John W. Apgar

In addition, the contributions of the following persons should be acknowledged. Mary June Erickson, language arts; Josephine J. Matthews, Dr. Marie Goldstein, and Dr. Gordon McLeod, mathematics; Marvin D. Patterson, science; Dr. Vincent N. Campbell, social studies; Sarah M. Russell, primary; Katheryn K. Woodley, Dr. Mary B. Willis, Debbra D. Michaels, performance standards; and Dr. Helen D. Dell, editorial

Final acknowledgment should go to those who use the objectives in these volumes. Objectives alone, an educational program do not make. They provide at best only a framework. The responsibility for the learning must rest on the student, guided by the teacher, and supervised by the school administration.

William M. Shanner

Palo Alto, California
December 15, 1970

INTRODUCTION

Although these volumes are mainly self-explanatory, the reader may find helpful the information that follows. The organization of the objectives is discussed, terms are defined, and the numbering system is clarified.

When a text is made up of many small parts, the constraints of print mean that each item has a fixed position on a page and within a volume, a position that establishes a sequential relationship with all preceding and following items regardless of whether such a relationship is logical or intentional. Since behavioral objectives may potentially be arranged in so many ways, it is important to understand how this collection is arranged and organized to avoid any unwarranted assumption that a prescriptive sequence is being suggested.

The objectives have been organized into four volumes, based on a natural, though often overlapping, grouping of the four major subject areas: language arts, social studies, mathematics, and science. Each volume ranges from Grade 1 through Grade 12. This arrangement is based on the needs of teachers and curriculum designers to perceive the span of a particular subject over the school years. An equally good argument can be made for presenting all the material across subjects for a single age level in one volume to emphasize the interrelatedness of the disciplines. The drawback of this format lies in the wide variations of curricula chosen in different local situations for a given age group. Subject-focused volumes, therefore, seem to be the most useful, with cross-referencing and cross-indexing to relate the subject areas.

Although each volume covers the traditional period from Grade 1 through Grade 12, grouping of objectives into single grade levels is inappropriate, again because of the flexibility of modern curriculum design. Instead, the objectives within each volume have been grouped according to Primary, Intermediate, and Secondary levels. The objectives in these groups overlap to some extent, but use of the three designations divides the objectives into sections of manageable size.

INTRODUCTION

These three groups, or levels, may be roughly defined as follows:

Primary: Primary refers to Grades 1 through 3 and covers the material that, in most cases, is presented in these three years. Some readiness material is included that covers preschool years. The more advanced material may be applicable to the Intermediate level; some objectives from the Intermediate level may be appropriate for late Primary.

Intermediate: Intermediate refers to the years usually included in Grades 4 through 8. Once again, this decision is arbitrary; curricula for Grades 7 and 8 are sometimes closely related to high-school studies. Where a junior high school includes Grades 7, 8, and 9, the Intermediate and the Secondary objectives need to be considered selectively.

Secondary: Secondary designates high school, from freshman through senior years. The material presumes that the student has covered the work included in the earlier grades. There is little or no re-presentation of review topics, nor are there objectives designed for remedial work.

Within subject areas there are many ways to subdivide material. It is important to have enough subdivisions to be meaningful and yet not so many that overlapping and confusion result.

The following lists show the topics selected for each volume.

LANGUAGE ARTS
- Listening Skills
- Speaking Skills
- Reading Skills
- Writing Skills
- Grammar Skills
- Study Skills
- Personal Communication and Development Skills
- History and Dialectology
- Classification, Interpretation, and Analysis of Literary Forms
- Original Writing
- Oral and Dramatic Interpretation
- Critical Analysis of Media

INTRODUCTION

SOCIAL STUDIES
- History
- Sociology and Anthropology
- Political Science
- Geography
- Economics
- Psychology and Philosophy
- Social Studies Inquiry Skills

SCIENCE
- Life Science
  - Biology (at secondary level only)
- Physical Science
  - Chemistry (at secondary level only)
  - Physics (at secondary level only)
- Earth Science
- Science Inquiry Skills

MATHEMATICS
- Analysis of Number and System
- Operations: Numerical and Algebraic
- Operations: Graphics
- Geometry
- Measurement and Probability
- Sets and Logic
- Problem Solving

The topics are useful here, but their sequence has no special significance. A sequence that appears logical to one curriculum designer may seem totally illogical to another. Printed material can never embody the flexibility that is possible in instruction. For example, in *Social Studies* the major topics occur in the same sequence through Primary, Intermediate, and Secondary levels. This sequence by no means implies that history should precede political science or economics in any one of these levels, since much instruction proceeds concurrently in various topics as well as in subject areas.

Another problem in writing objectives lies in breaking the material into appropriate learning "chunks." An objective can be so broad that it is meaningless, or it can represent such a small sample of behavior that the instructional program appears to proceed at a snail's pace.

INTRODUCTION

Behavioral Objectives: A Guide to Individualizing Learning approaches this quandary by selecting major benchmarks in student progress. These have been designated Terminal Objectives; subsumed under these, Transitional Objectives group the Terminal Objectives into smaller units.

A Terminal Objective represents a major growth point in student progress, the culmination of work done over a period of time. It can be tested through a project undertaken by a student as in a social-studies investigation, or it may be measured by a test that presents a variety of problems as defined in the objective.

Transitional Objectives lead the student to mastery of the Terminal Objective. Decisions regarding the amount to be mastered in a Transitional Objective may appear to have been made on an arbitrary basis. Sometimes small categories have been grouped into an objective that represents a fairly large area of behavior. Other objectives may seem overly small. Once again, it must be emphasized that these objectives serve as guidlines, not as prescriptions.

Numbering System: Each Terminal Objective is identified by a subject-area designator—LA for language arts, SS for social studies, MA for mathematics, and SC for science—and a three-digit number. The numbers begin with 005 and continue at intervals of five, with a few exceptions, so that new Terminal Objectives can be inserted without rearrangement of the numbering system. In final editing of these volumes such interpolations were made, and the new numbers were assigned sequentially. In each subject area Primary begins with 005, Intermediate with 200, and Secondary with 500. Since numbers were assigned after the objectives were assembled, they do not represent a prescribed sequence.

For those who are interested in making a more comprehensive numbering system, a two-decimal designator can be added for each of the Transitional Objectives that follows a Terminal Objective. (In the present collection no set of Transitional Objectives exceeds 99.) For computer purposes, each of the lettered subject-area designators may be assigned a number: 1, 2, 3, 4.

In this way a six-digit code can be constructed to identify any objective by subject area or by age group. Addition of a seventh digit would permit identification of the cognitive level as well.

INTRODUCTION

Cross-references: To show the interrelatedness of these objectives, some cross-referencing has been indicated by numbers in parentheses that refer to Terminal Objectives. The letter designator shows whether reference is made to an objective in the same area or to one in another subject area. These cross-references can only suggest the wide possibilities of relating various topics.

Cognitive level: Behavioral objectives are often criticized for their seeming triviality and the fact that many of them call upon memorization and application of learned facts. In an effort to test the objectives in these volumes, a modified approach to Bloom's *Taxonomy of Educational Objectives, Cognitive Domain* was applied, using six cognitive levels. This evaluation proved a revealing indication of how well these objectives are distributed among the cognitive levels. For this reason the cognitive level has been included and is indicated by a roman numeral following each objective.

Each Terminal Objective has been carefully phrased to indicate specifically the cognitive level expected. Transitional Objectives do not follow a rigidly consistent pattern, but wherever possible the verbs were selected from the lists related to the cognitive levels.

The following phrases and verbs have been used:
LEVEL I: KNOWLEDGE. Emphasis is on recall, whether of specifics or universals. Terminal Objective: Show that you know (about) . . .

Transitional Objectives for Level I for the most part use the following verbs: answer questions, choose, define, finish, complete, follow directions, identify, indicate, label, list, locate, match, select.

LEVEL II: COMPREHENSION. Emphasis is on grasp of meaning, intent, or relationship in oral, written, graphic, or nonverbal communication. Terminal Objective: Show your understanding of . . . (by) . . .

In Transitional Objectives the following verbs are used: classify, compare the importance of (not just *compare,* which is Level VI), derive, describe, estimate, expand, explain, express, interpret, measure, put in order, recognize, suggest, summarize, trace, convert, add, balance, calculate, compute, divide, factor, multiply, subtract, write numerals.

INTRODUCTION

LEVEL III: APPLICATION. Emphasis is on applying appropriate principles or generalizations. Terminal Objective: Show that you can use or apply . . .

Transitional Objectives draw mainly on these words: apply, compute, construct, make, draw, demonstrate, differentiate, discuss, express in a discussion, find, use, collect information, keep records, participate, perform, plan, predict, prepare, present, solve (word problems, problem situations), use.

LEVEL IV: ANALYSIS. Emphasis is on breakdown into constituent parts and detection of relationships of the parts and of the way they are organized. This level is often an aid to comprehension or a prelude to evaluation. Terminal Objective: Demonstrate your ability to perceive . . . (the parts of/relationship between) . . . (Words in parentheses can be implied or stated in terms of specifics.)

Transitional Objectives draw from this list: analyze, debate, determine, differentiate, form generalizations, deduce, draw conclusions, make inferences, organize.

LEVEL V: SYNTHESIS. Emphasis is on putting together elements or parts to form a whole not clearly there before the student performance. Terminal Objective: Demonstrate your ability to combine concepts, principles and generalizations.

Transitional objectives usually include one of the following verbs: combine and organize, design, develop, produce, write (an original composition).

LEVEL VI: EVALUATION. Emphasis is on values, making qualitative or quantitative judgments with criteria from internal or external sources and with standards. Terminal Objective: Make a judgment on . . . or involving . . .

Transitional Objectives are built around these verbs: compare (and contrast), make a decision, decide, evaluate.

The reader or user is encouraged to criticize the application of cognitive levels in relation to accuracy of application as well as to appropriateness for the particular topic or age group. Like all other facets of these objectives, the listing of cognitive level is designed to stimulate thought regarding the instructional program.

PRIMARY

LIFE SCIENCE

SC 005 Show your understanding of the properties of a given plant or animal. II

Describe the properties of a plant or part of a plant. II

Describe the change of properties in a growing plant. II

Record the changing properties of a growing plant. II

Classify animals according to habitats, skin covering, the way the animal moves, and/or the number of legs. II

Identify the following properties of animals: (1) how they eat, (2) how they grow, (3) how they change, (4) how they move by themselves, and (5) how they have babies. I

Record the growth changes of an animal you have observed. II (SC 075)

Classify familiar animals according to whether they eat meat, plants, or both. II

SC 010 Show that you know about the functions of the ear, eye, nose, and tongue. I

Identify the functions of the following organs: (1) the ear, (2) the eye, (3) the nose, and (4) the tongue.

Label the parts of the ear and tell their functions: (1) outer ear, (2) middle ear, (3) inner ear, (4) pinna, (5) ear canal, (6) eardrum, (7) hammer, (8) anvil, (9) cochlea, and (10) nerve. I

Label the parts of the eye and tell their functions: (1) eyelid, (2) eyelashes, (3) iris, (4) pupil, and (5) tear duct. I

SC 015 Show your understanding of the senses by classifying objects according to smell, taste, touch, sight, and sound. II

Describe the shape and texture of unseen objects by using the sense of touch. II

Classify circles, triangles, squares, and rectangles by shape. II

After touching an object, describe its texture. II

Classify objects by texture. II

Recognize a circle, a square, a triangle, and a rectangle by using the sense of touch. II

Classify objects by size using only the sense of touch. II

Classify objects by temperature using the sense of touch (warm, hot, cold). II

Classify objects by temperature using a thermometer. II

Classify objects by weight. II

Classify objects by smell. II

Given objects that look alike but differ in smell or taste, recognize the difference. II

Given various foods to taste, classify their tastes as salty, sour, sweet, or bitter. II

Classify objects by taste. II

Name the primary colors. I

Recognize the primary colors. II

Identify the secondary color that results from the combination of two primary colors. I

Classify objects by color. II

PRIMARY

Recognize objects that make sounds you can hear. II

Classify objects by the sounds they make. II

Given one sound followed by another sound, recognize which sound is more pleasant. II

Given one sound followed by another sound, recognize which sound is louder. Use the same instrument and same volume, but vary the pitch. II

Identify the sense or senses used in examining a given object. I

SC 020 Show your understanding of the differences in animal reproduction. II

Classify animal mothers into (1) mothers who have living babies, and (2) mothers who lay eggs. II

Identify the terms *male, female, parent,* and *offspring* when discussing members of animal families. I

Match animal parents to their offspring. I (SC 005)

Recognize when a picture of an insect is in an adult, egg, larva, or pupa stage. Recognize the order in which these stages occur. II

Recognize when a frog is in an adult, egg, or tadpole stage. Recognize the order in which these stages occur. II

SC 025 Show that you know about interaction of organisms with their environment. I

Tell the things soil must have to make plants grow well. I

Tell the ways plants help make good soil. I

Conduct an experiment in which you try to grow similar seeds under two or more different soil conditions. III (SC 080)

Tell what factors influence the growth of an organism. I

Tell ways that animals help to make good soil. I

Tell how soil helps animals. I

Tell what should be added to the class aquarium to keep the aquarium balanced. I

Indicate how things in an aquarium interact to keep the aquarium balanced. I

Demonstrate through sequencing of photographs, drawings, or written explanations the meaning of "food chain." Include dependence on the sun. III

Use pictures or real examples to demonstrate findings about how organisms interact in their environment. III

PHYSICAL SCIENCE

SC 030 Show that you know about simple machines by identifying them in groups of pictures or examples. I

Identify definitions of a simple machine. I

Tell the benefits of simple machines. I

Recognize which type of simple machine—inclined plane, wedge, lever—is used in a given situation. II

Recognize which type of simple machine—pulley, screw, or wheel—is used in a given situation. II

Recognize the simple machines you have observed in your own home. II

Predict whether an object that is on rollers or wheels moves more or less easily than an object that is not on rollers or wheels. Test to see if you were right. III

PRIMARY

Identify gears on an object. I

Identify the faster gear on an object with two gears. I

Predict whether an object with a pulley will move more or less easily than an object without a pulley. Test to see if you were right. III

Predict in which direction a pulley cord should be pulled to make an object move up or down. Test to see if you were right. III

Identify pulley systems in everyday objects. I

Given such simple materials as spools and a rope, construct a pulley system that will work. III

SC 035 Show your understanding of objects by classifying them according to type, form, and properties. II

Identify the sense or senses used in examining a given object. I

Recognize the heavier of two objects when they are placed in the pans of an equal-arm balance. II (MA 080)

Given a standard unit of weight and a solid object, predict how many of the standard units represent the weight of the object. III (MA 080)

Describe the texture, weight, size, shape, color, and reflectance of a given object. II

Classify a group of objects according to (1) texture, (2) weight, (3) size, (4) shape, (5) color, and (6) reflectance. II

Classify samples of birch, walnut, and oak according to the type of wood. II

Recognize the chips, sawdust, and shavings of a given kind of wood. II

Classify wood, metal, and plastic objects according to the type of material. II

Describe some properties of a given object: (1) color, (2) magnetism, (3) weight, (4) material, (5) shape, (6) texture. II

Classify rocks by size, color, kind, hardness, and weight. II

Recognize the rock form and the powder form of a given kind of mineral. II

Classify liquids by density and opaqueness. II

Tell, after observation, whether a given object floats or sinks in water. I

Identify the liquid form and the ice form of water. I

Identify the evidence of air as an object. I

Keep an accurate record that shows classification of objects used in an experiment and the results of the experiment. III (SC 075)

SC 040 Show your understanding of forms of energy. II

Explain how an experiment shows that heat is a form of energy. II

Given objects, predict which object is a heat conductor and which object is not. Explain the reasons for your predictions. Test to see if you were right. III (SC 080)

Identify definitions of light and sound and tell how they travel (i.e., speed through air, water, solids, etc.). I

Given a series of pictures of objects or actual objects, recognize whether the object produces or reflects light. II

Describe how sounds are different when they are made by different objects. II

SC 045 Show your understanding of interactions in the physical world. II

Identify interacting objects in demonstrations or pictures. I

Using various senses, find evidence of interaction. II

PRIMARY

Find evidence of interaction by relating aspects of similar experiments. II

Recognize evidence of interaction in demonstrations or pictures. II

Recognize conservation within a system in which objects change in appearance. II

Identify systems of objects that interact at a distance. I

Classify systems of objects according to whether or not they show evidence of interaction at a distance. II

Identify the sense or senses used to observe magnetic interaction at a distance (seeing, hearing, smelling). I

Keep an accurate record of objects you have observed interacting at a distance. III (SC 075)

Explain why an electrical circuit is a system of interacting objects. II

Identify open and closed circuits. I

Predict whether or not an object will close an open circuit. III

SC 050 Show your understanding of relationships of objects and interactions in systems. II

Apply the word *system* to a group of related objects and recognize the common elements of objects that make them part of that system. III

Recognize systems of interacting objects. II

Record objects belonging to a system. II

Identify definitions and examples of systems. I

Identify definitions and examples of subsystems. I

Recognize the evidence of interaction in a system or a subsystem. II

Name the parts of a solution that are subsystems of that solution. I

Name the parts of a filtering system and define their functions. I

earth science

SC 055 Show your understanding of the solar system in terms of rotation and revolution of the earth and in terms of properties of the sun and the earth. II (SC 180)

Tell the difference between rotation and revolution of the earth. I

Recognize the effects of rotation and revolution of the earth. Use a globe to relate these phenomena to changes in hours of daylight and in the type of season on a given area of earth. II (SS 180)

Describe the size, shape, color, state of matter, and temperature of the sun and the earth. II

SC 060 Show your understanding of a diagram that illustrates the soil-making process. II

Explain the different ways that rock is broken down to become soil. II

Given a cross-section of soils, recognize the layers as topsoil, subsoil, and bedrock. II

Describe the things found in dark topsoil that are not found in sand and subsoil. II

SC 065 Show your understanding of relationships of ideas and objects to prehistoric life. II

Tell what *extinct* means. Tell why dinosaurs are extinct. I

Tell possible geographic reasons that prehistoric plants and animals are no longer living. I

Tell what a fossil is. Tell what we learn from fossils. I

After visiting a museum of natural history and observing the exhibits of dinosaur skeletons, bones, and fossils, describe what you saw for a group of students. II

SCIENCE INQUIRY SKILLS

SC 070 Demonstrate that you can collect information, through reading and interviewing, about the interaction of organisms with their environment. III

SC 075 Demonstrate that you can keep records of observation, reading, and interviewing in the form of lists, notes, or pictures. III

SC 080 Demonstrate that you can conduct a simple experiment, making observations, keeping records, and relating the results to a given hypothesis. III

(Transitional Objectives for Science Inquiry Skills appear under the various subject topics as appropriate.)

LIFE SCIENCE

SC 200 Given a drawing of the human body, show that you know about body systems and body parts. I

In a drawing, identify these bones: (1) skull, (2) backbone, (3) ribs, (4) shoulder blade, (5) upper arm bone, (6) lower arm bones, (7) hipbone, (8) thighbone, (9) kneecap, (10) shinbone, (11) heel bone, (12) toe and finger bones. I

Identify the following on a drawing of the digestive system: (1) mouth, (2) teeth, (3) tongue, (4) food pipe, (5) stomach, and (6) intestine. I

Given a diagram of the human skeleton, locate the major bone areas that form the framework of the body: (1) skull, (2) rib cage, (3) backbone, (4) pelvis, (5) femur, (6) tibia, (7) fibula, (8) radius, (9) ulna, and (10) phalanges. I

Given a diagram of the digestive system, label the parts and identify the function of each. Include (1) salivary glands, (2) mouth, (3) general esophagus, (4) sphincter muscles, (5) stomach, (6) gall bladder, (7) liver, (8) pancreas, (9) large intestine, (10) small intestine, (11) appendix, and (12) rectum. I

Given a diagram of part of the human circulatory system and a description of the function of the parts shown, identify the following: (1) heart, (2) capillary, (3) artery, (4) vein, (5) arteriole, and (6) capillary. I

SC 205 Show your understanding of the human body by matching the names of human body systems and body parts to a description of their major functions. II

Explain how opposing muscles, including those of the arm and leg, work to cause movement of body parts. II

Given the terms *arteries, veins, capillaries,* and *heart,* describe how blood travels in the body. II

Describe the normal flow of air in and out of the human respiratory system. Include the following terms: *lungs, nose, nasal passage,* and *windpipe.* II

INTERMEDIATE

Match the systems of the human body—digestive, circulatory, respiratory, nervous, reproductive, glandular, excretory, skeletal, muscular, and skin—with the important general functions of each. I

Given a diagram of a skeleton, locate four kinds of joints: (1) hinge joints, (2) ball-and-socket joints, (3) immovable joints, and (4) pivot joints. I

Identify the locations and functions of the major parts of the central nervous system: (1) the brain (cerebellum, cerebrum, and medulla), and (2) the spinal cord. I

Define *peristalsis* and identify its role in digestion and egestion. I

Define enzyme and identify the specific function of each of the following digestive enzymes: (1) amylase, (2) pepsin, (3) trypsin, (4) chymotrypsin, (5) peptidase, (6) dipeptidase, (7) maltase, (8) sucrase, (9) lactase, and (10) lipase. I

Describe the structures and functions of the organs in man's digestive system and in the digestive system of each of the following animals: (1) amoeba, (2) hydra, (3) earthworm, (4) clam, (5) grasshopper, (6) bee, (7) spider, (8) bird, (9) fish, and (10) frog. II

Given a diagram of the respiratory system, label the following parts and identify the function of each: (1) epiglottis, (2) larynx, (3) trachea, (4) lung, (5) bronchus, (6) air sacs, and (7) diaphragm. I

Identify the location of the following endocrine glands in the human body, and identify the secretion(s) produced by each gland and the body function that each secretion controls: (1) pituitary, (2) thyroid, (3) parathyroid, (4) pancreas, (5) adrenal cortex, (6) adrenal medulla, (7) male reproductive organs, and (8) female reproductive organs. I

Given a diagram of the excretory system for liquid waste, label the following parts and identify the function of each part: (1) post-caval vein, (2) renal artery, (3) kidney, (4) renal vein, (5) ureter, (6) blood vessels to leg, and (7) bladder. I

INTERMEDIATE

Identify the major constituent differences between whole blood and blood plasma. Identify the major functions of each in the body and the purpose they serve in transfusions. I

Explain the differences between blood and lymph, including their parts and major functions in the human body. II

Given a model or a picture of the human eye, explain the function and operation of the main parts and the overall function of the whole organ. II

Given a model or a picture of the human ear, explain the function and operation of the main parts and the overall function of the whole organ. I

Given a model or a picture of the human tongue, explain the function and operation of the parts and the overall function of the whole organ. I

SC 210 Show your understanding of basic human needs by recognizing items necessary to maintaining a healthy existence. II (SS 090)

From a list of foods, identify the best sources of each of the following nutrients: carbohydrate, fat, and protein. I

Conduct tests to find out whether a food is mainly a carbohydrate, a fat, or a protein. III (SC 390)

Classify a familiar food as belonging to one of the following: (1) milk group; (2) meat group; (3) bread-cereal group; or (4) vegetable-fruit group. II

Explain whether the food eaten in one day by a child constitutes a balanced diet. If it does not, tell what is missing. II

Tell why a person needs nutrients and how they differ from wastes. I

Match an essential nutrient with the food that can provide a major amount of that nutrient. I

Name two health reasons for good posture and tell if a person is showing proper posture in standing, walking, and sitting. I

Explain how to take proper care of teeth, hair, nails, and the skin of the face and hands. Name two reasons why each of these routines is important. II

List at least seven examples of good health and safety precautions (e.g. brushing teeth, not riding on bicycle handlebars) and explain why you should or should not be responsible for each item listed. II

Plan a well-balanced diet for one day. III

From a list of statements, identify statements that describe health conditions in an underdeveloped nation. Make up a story about the health problems in an imaginary underdeveloped nation. III

Describe technological advances that permit man to counteract each of the following conditions to establish a closed ecosystem in a space craft: (1) lack of gravity, (2) absence of food, (3) decreased air pressure, (4) extremes of temperature, and (5) lack of oxygen. II

Suggest a schedule of exercise to help an individual remain healthy. II

SC 215 Show your understanding of the characteristics of given organisms that are harmful to man. II

Explain the structures and functions of four general groups of disease-causing microorganisms: (1) virus, (2) fungus, (3) bacteria, and (4) protozoa. II

Correctly label given drawings or descriptions of each of the three types of bacteria: (1) coccus, (2) bacillus, and (3) spirillum. I

Given a sentence describing some activities of a microorganism (e.g., bacteria, protozoa, viruses), tell whether the activities are helpful or harmful to man. I

Given examples of common household or professional medical practices, tell whether chemicals, heat, or antibiotics are being used to combat infectious bacteria. I

INTERMEDIATE

Given a list of scientists who have studied microorganisms (Louis Pasteur, Edward Jenner, Joseph Lister, Jonas Salk, Alexander Fleming, Robert Koch) and their scientific discoveries, match the scientist with his discovery. I

Explain the differences in the following types of diseases: (1) organic, (2) allergic, (3) infectious, (4) deficiency. I

Given a description of a particular disease and the way it is contracted, classify the disease as communicable or noncommunicable. II

Explain the ways in which specific disease-causing organisms enter the body: (1) entry with water, milk, or food, (2) entry with the air, and (3) entry through the skin. List one means of preventing each of these problems. II

Explain the body's lines of defense that help in resisting and/or combating disease-causing microorganisms. II

Identify the most effective methods used to prevent the spread of disease. I

SC 220 Show that you can collect information about and discuss human diseases. III

Summarize six articles from magazines or newspapers about research that scientists are doing on at least one disease. Present an oral or written report on your findings. III (LA 260)

Identify the ways in which each of the following are harmful to man: (1) rickettsiae, (2) fungi, (3) bacteria, (4) viruses, (5) protozoa, and (6) algae. I

Identify the ways in which each of the following organisms are helpful to man: (1) fungi, (2) viruses, (3) protozoa, (4) algae, and (5) bacteria. I

Identify diagrams or descriptions of poison ivy, poison oak, poison sumac, and wild mushrooms. Tell the dangerous effect that each of these plants can have on man. I

Define each of the following and identify examples of each when described: *symbiosis, parasitism, mutualism,* and *commensalism.* I

Prepare and present a report tracing the research history of diabetes and insulin. Include a description of the contributions that each of the following scientists made to the discovery and use of insulin: (1) Von Mering, (2) Minkowski, (3) Banting, (4) MacCleod, and (5) Best. Also include any recent information on diabetes reported by medical research. III (LA 260)

Prepare and present an oral report or prepare diagrams and pictures about a disease in which you are interested. Trace the research done by scientists on the disease throughout the last fifty years. III (LA 345)

Define the term *communicable disease* and tell whether each of the following diseases is communicable or noncommunicable. I

1. Colds
2. Influenza
3. Measles
4. Chicken pox
5. Smallpox
6. Whooping cough
7. Mumps
8. Poliomyelitis
9. Psittacosis
10. Typhoid fever
11. Dysentery
12. Cholera
13. Tetanus
14. Gas gangrene
15. Botulism
16. Anthrax
17. Rabies
18. Tularemia

Identify the type of organism (bacterium, virus, or protozoan) that causes each of the following diseases, and describe the method(s) of transmission and prevention for each disease. II

1. Tuberculosis
2. Diphtheria
3. Typhoid
4. Scarlet fever
5. Meningitis
6. Whooping cough

SC 225 Show that you can collect information about and discuss the effects of tobacco, alcohol, and drugs on the human body, using reliable reports of research. III (LA 330, SS 270)

From a given description of symptoms, recognize symptoms that describe the physiological effects of smoking on the human body. II

INTERMEDIATE

Identify three ways to help a smoker stop his habit. I

From a given description of symptoms, recognize symptoms that describe the physiological effects of alcohol on the human body. II

Identify the path alcohol takes as it is absorbed into the blood stream and identify three principal parts of the body that are adversely affected. I

Identify at least three reasons that people who drink alcoholic beverages give to justify their actions. I

Identify three steps that a moderate drinker can take to prevent himself from becoming an alcoholic. I

From a given description of symptoms, recognize symptoms that describe the psychological effects of specific drugs on the human body. II

Identify proper and improper uses of (1) amphetamines, and (2) depressants. I

Identify at least one possible immediate physiological effect and one possible aftereffect on human beings who use marijuana. I

Identify two ways in which the improper use of drugs might be avoided. II

Identify at least three reasons given by drug users to justify their use of drugs. I

Explain steps that might be taken to rehabilitate alcoholics or drug addicts. III (SS 285)

SC 230 Show that you can use selected diagrams, pictures, or models to demonstrate the adaptive powers of plants and animals. III

Identify a definition of *habitat.* Match organisms with pictures, descriptions, or names of the habitats to which they are best adapted. I

INTERMEDIATE

Tell what most organisms need to stay alive. I

Match definitions with the following terms: *birth, death, survive, adapt,* and *extinct.* I

Match mouth adaptations to kinds of food to be gathered by an animal. I

Match the breathing structure (lungs or gills) of a common animal to the habitat for which it is best suited. I

Match illustrations of the following animal structures with the task for which they are best suited. I

Structures	*Tasks*
Claws, webbed feet	Walking, swimming
Hoofs, toes	Running, flying
Wings, fins	Climbing, perching
	Balancing

Tell how body coverings help animals to adapt to certain climates. I

Match descriptions or drawings of seeds with the means (including wind, water, or animals such as birds, mammals, and man) by which they travel from the parent plant to another plant. I

Given a description or illustration of the coloring of an animal and the animal's habitat, explain whether or not the animal would survive by blending with its habitat. II

Identify some of the reasons why animals migrate. I

Identify the methods and tools that man uses to track the migration routes of birds. I

Identify correct statements of what happens within the body during hibernation, and identify from a list those animals that hibernate. I

INTERMEDIATE

Prepare and present a report on the following animal societies on the basis of the degree of organization of the members within the society: (1) ants, (2) bees, (3) wasps, (4) wolves, (5) elephants, (6) deer, and (7) termites. III

SC 235 Show your understanding of characteristics and functions of plant and animal cells. II

Given a simple slide and a microscope, classify objects on the slide as cells or objects that are not cells (e.g., air bubbles, dirt, crystals). II

Identify from a list that names cell structures, or from a group of pictures or slides of living tissue that exhibit cell structures, those cellular characteristics that are present (1) only in plant cells, (2) only in animal cells, or (3) in both. I

Given diagrams of generalized animal cells and plant cells, identify the parts that are (1) common to each, (2) possessed only by the plant cell, and (3) possessed only by the animal cell. I

Explain the interrelationships that exist among the following structures: (1) cell, (2) tissue, (3) organ, (4) system, (5) organism. Base the identification on the degree of complexity of their organization. II

Identify the materials that cells require to maintain life. I

Observe plant and animal cells under the microscope. (Use your own nail, skin, or blood cells.) Describe as many differences as you can observe. II

Given descriptions of ways in which substances move through cell membranes, identify each as (1) passive diffusion, (2) active transport, or (3) ingestion. I

Identify the factors that affect the rate at which a solid solute goes into a liquid solvent. I (SC 390)

Suggest an experiment to test the permeability of several types of material. II (SC 390)

INTERMEDIATE

SC 240 Show that you can use scientific classifications to classify given plants and animals. III (SC 395)

Given a description or an example of a plant, classify it into one of these major groups: (1) simple plants, (2) mosses, (3) ferns, or (4) seed plant (including plants with cones and plants with flowers). II

On the basis of distinct characteristics, classify common animals as belonging to one of the following groups: (1) worms, (2) insects, (3) shellfish, (4) fish, (5) amphibians, (6) reptiles, (7) bird, or (8) mammals. II

Given the name of a specific kingdom, phylum, or class and examples of animals found in the group named, identify the characteristics common to this group of animals. I

Given names, pictures, or specimens of animals, match them with a classification system involving at least two groups. III

On the basis of evolutionary changes in the body structure that have occurred over the ages, describe the ancestral and modern version of each of the following organisms: horse, dog, and man. II

Given various objects, classify them on the basis of specific given criteria. II

Identify the proper sequence of categories from kingdom to species in the Linnaean System of classification. I

Explain why the category of organisms called Protista has recently been made a separate kingdom of biological classification. II

Identify the structural characteristics used to classify living organisms into these three kingdoms: Animalia, Plantae, Protista. I

Draw a family tree to represent the evolutionary changes of an animal with which you are familiar. In a written, oral, or pictorial report describe the characteristics that were purposely bred into the animal. III

INTERMEDIATE

SC 245 Demonstrate your ability to combine concepts, principles, and generalizations by designing an investigation of a biological problem that involves the use of the microscope and other tools of the modern biologist. V (SC 385)

Explain the maintenance and operation of the compound-monocular microscope. II

Identify a correct statement of the function served by such instruments as the microscope and the thermometer in scientific observation. I

Given descriptions of particular attitudes or beliefs, describe those that have been formed after scientific observation and those based upon previously formed or untested beliefs. II

Given a description of a biological experiment, recognize the following stages in its development: (1) discovery of the problem, (2) gathering information, (3) formation of a testable hypothesis, (4) performance of an experiment to test the hypothesis, and (5) interpretation of the results and formation of conclusions. II (SC 390)

Given a scientific event or situation, suggest questions that would help to explain the event or situation and suggest sources of information or activities that may lead to an answer to the question. II

Develop hypothesis based on observations and inferences drawn from biological science. (A hypothesis is an idea stated in such a way that it can be tested.) V (SC 390)

Given a hypothesis that can be tested, design a laboratory procedure, or experiment, that will test the hypothesis. III

After observing objects and events in the field of biology, using each of your five senses as appropriate, record the observations in terms of amounts whenever possible. II

Given a statement of observations from an experiment, classify each as a qualitative observation or a quantitative observation. II

Given the results of a laboratory procedure, or experiment, record them and display them in tabular and graphic form. II

Describe the factual information displayed in a graph. II

Explain the way two variables on a graph of biological data are related. II

SC 250 Show your understanding of the reproductive process in plants, insects, and animals. II (SS 265)

Identify the fruit and the four main parts (roots, stems, leaves, flowers) of a flowering plant and explain the basic function of the main parts. II

Define each of the following: (1) fission, (2) budding, (3) spore formation, (4) regeneration, and (5) vegetative reproduction. Recognize drawings or descriptions of each. I

Identify each of the following parts of a flower and tell the function of each part: (1) stamen, (2) anther, (3) stigma, (4) pollen, (5) style, (6) pistil, (7) ovary, (8) petal, (9) sepal, and (10) filaments. I

Recognize the body parts of a mealworm—antenna, head, mouth, leg, thorax, abdomen—and describe their functions. II

Identify the body parts of an insect you choose to study. II

Define each of the following stages: adult, larva, egg, and pupa. Identify examples of these stages in the metamorphosis of a butterfly, a fly, and a mosquito. I

Recognize the difference between complete and incomplete metamorphosis. II

Keep a record of your observations of the developmental stages. III

Identify correct definitions of *reproduction* and differentiate between the characteristics of sexual and asexual reproduction. I

Describe the conditions of birth, the appearance of the newborn, and the life requirements of the newborn of each of the following animals: (1) man, (2) dog, (3) chicken, (4) turtle, (5) fish, and (6) frog. II

INTERMEDIATE

SC 255 Show that you can discuss the human reproductive system. III (SS 265)

Given the names of the reproductive organs in man and in a flowering plant, identify the organs that perform the same function(s) and tell the function that each performs. I

Given a list of bodily changes, identify the following changes as those that occur in males or females during puberty: (1) growth of hair on the face, (2) changes in the voice, (3) rapid growth of long bones, (4) general increase of body hair, (5) development of breasts, (6) onset of menstruation, (7) widening of hips, and (8) rapid growth in height and weight. I

Given a diagram, identify the following human male reproductive organs and the function of each: (1) testes, (2) penis, (3) urethra, (4) scrotum, and (5) sperm ducts. I

Given a diagram identify the following human female reproductive organs and the function of each: (1) ovaries, (2) Fallopian tubes, (3) vagina, and (4) uterus. I

Recognize correct definitions of each of the following terms and explain the relationship of each to the total development of a person: (1) birth, (2) blastula, (3) coitus, (4) fertilization, (5) fetus, (6) gametes, (7) gastrula, and (8) zygote. II

Write a report (or report orally) on the profession of a geneticist. Include information on research geneticists might conduct. III

Support or refute suggestions for altering the reproductive patterns of people. III

SC 260 Given the continuation of the expansion of cities and the destruction of natural life, show that you can reasonably predict the change that will be apparent in the total environment. Report evidence to support your predictions. III (SS 265, LA 335)

Predict which of several experiments is best designed to answer a given question about the effect of such variables as temperature, air supply, light, water, and food on behavior or growth of an organism in its environment. III (SC 390)

INTERMEDIATE

Support the following hypothesis by experimental procedures. If one of the reactants (variables) is removed from the photosynthesis reaction in green plants, then these plants cannot produce food. III (SC 390)

Recognize a correct drawing of the carbon cycle and describe the functional interrelationships among the parts of the cycle. II

Recognize a correct drawing of the nitrogen cycle and describe the functional interrelationships among the parts of the cycle. II

Explain the difference between a food chain and a food web, and describe the interrelationships of food chains in a food web. II

Define the terms *predator, parasite,* and *scavenger* and identify examples of each. I

Explain the effects that the removal of one part of a food web would have on the total environment of a given habitat. II

Given an example of a food chain, trace the flow of energy through the chain and relate the following terms to the correct type of organism when involved: *producer, consumer, saprophyte,* and *predator.* II

Given a description of characteristics of a plant or plant products, explain how the plant products are useful or beneficial to man. II

Predict the response of a particular plant to specific growing conditions. Apply the conditions in an experiment. Write a laboratory report on the result. III (SC 390)

Given information on the interrelationship of living things in a pond, describe the benefits of one plant or animal to the other animals and other plants. II

Review information from any sources that demonstrates the absence of an organism necessary to maintain a balance of interrelation between plants and animals in a particular area. Suggest a plan for correcting the imbalance in the environment. II

Identify the main forces that erode the soil and tell how each force contributes to the erosion. I

INTERMEDIATE

Define the term *conservation* and identify ways of preventing soil erosion. I

Match listed causes of air pollution to related forms of prevention. I

Match listed causes of water pollution to related forms of prevention. I

Prepare a demonstration of soil erosion. Record the changes in the original topology of your example as you alter the forces on the soil. III (SC 400)

PHYSICAL SCIENCE

SC 265 Show your understanding of the relative positions of stationary and moving objects. II (SC 400)

Describe the position of an object relative to other objects. II

Describe the position of an object as seen by another person. II

Tell which way an object has moved relative to you and a reference object. I

Describe the direction of movement that an object has as seen by another observer relative to the position of that observer. The description could include reference to another object or system. II

Recognize evidence of motion in photographs, motion pictures, or flip-book pictures by reporting differential speeds of pictured objects that have apparent motion. Identify changes in the position of pictured objects relative to specified reference objects. II

Given illustrations of two objects or systems that have different rates of motion, recognize which object or system is moving faster and which is moving slower. II (MA 420)

Recognize whether or not an object has moved relative to another object. II

INTERMEDIATE

SC 270 Demonstrate your ability to combine concepts, principles, and generalizations by designing three experiments that show (1) the increase or decrease of the speed of an object, and (2) velocity as a function of time. V (MA 375, MA 385, SC 400)

Given a description or an illustration of a situation that involves an object rolling or sliding from one surface to another, predict whether the speed of the object will increase or decrease and whether a change in direction is likely to occur. III

Given a description of an object changing velocity, construct a graph that shows velocity as a function of time and predict changes in velocity with respect to time. Explain positive acceleration and negative acceleration or deceleration. III

SC 275 Given a demonstration of a moving object, show that you can use these terms to explain the phenomena: *force, inertia, energy, work, friction.* **III**

Identify acceptable definitions for the terms *force, inertia,* and *weight.* I

Demonstrate your understanding of the term *force* and apply the term in describing situations where push or pull is exerted on an object. III (SC 400)

From observation of an experiment, recognize proof showing that to act against a certain gravitational force (weight) requires an equal amount of force. II (SC 390)

Recognize examples of inertia shown in experiments. II

Identify the variables that affect the swing of a pendulum and tell how the swing is affected by these variables. I

From a list of common objects recognize those that are in a state of potential energy (stored energy) and those that are in a state of kinetic energy (energy of motion). II

Explain what form of energy (mechanical, chemical, heat, light, sound, electrical) and/or what state of energy (kinetic or potential) different objects have, use, or produce that make it possible for them to do work. II

INTERMEDIATE

Given a description of an energy change, explain whether it has been a transformation in the form or the state of the energy and/or name the form or state to which it has been changed. II

SC 280 Given a description or a diagram, show your understanding of atoms, elements, molecules, compounds, and mixtures. II

Identify an acceptable definition of the terms *matter, molecule, atom, electron,* and *neutron.* I

Given a list of early theories on matter, match each theory with the scientist who furthered it: (1) Dalton, (2) Boyle, (3) Democritus, (4) Empedocles. I

Interpret information obtained from simple experimental tests to identify elements. II (SC 390)

Explain the difference between an atom and a molecule when given a diagram, drawing, or description of each. II

Classify common substances as elements or compounds when given symbols, formulas, or models. II (SC 395)

Classify substances (e.g., sugar, salt, glass) as crystalline or noncrystalline when given a description or drawing of the molecular arrangements. II (SC 395)

From a given definition or description of a substance, recognize the substance as a compound or a mixture. II

SC 285 Show that you can construct a model of an element showing the relationship between the atomic number of the element and the number of electrons in an atom of the element. III (SC 400)

Recognize the relationship between the atomic number of an element and the number of electrons in the atom of the element. II

SC 290 Show that you can use water to demonstrate the three phases of matter. Explain the changes at the molecular level and describe the properties at each phase. III (SC 390)

Demonstrate one way to show that matter takes up space. III (SC 400)

Demonstrate one way to show that matter has weight. III (SC 400, MA 385)

Recognize several properties of an object or a substance, including (1) color, (2) shape, (3) size, (4) texture, (5) taste, (6) odor, and (7) state of matter. Recognize the sense used to determine each of these properties. II (SC 395)

Given a situation in which an object or substance must fit into a prescribed space or conform to a given weight capacity, explain whether it is more important to know about the material's weight or its volume. II (MA 385)

Given a list of substances, identify each substance as a gas, a liquid, or a solid. I

Describe a solid, a liquid, and a gas in terms of definite or indefinite volume and shape. II

Explain the relative motion of the molecules and the relative distances between the molecules in the solid, liquid, and gaseous phases of matter. II

Identify the points of phase change and describe the processes involved: (1) boiling, (2) boiling point, (3) freezing, (4) freezing point, (5) melting, (6) melting point, (7) sublimation, (8) condensation, (9) vaporization. II

Explain how plasma differs from solids, liquids, and gases. Given a list of substances, recognize those that are plasma. II

SC 295 Show that you can demonstrate the effects of heat on matter. Describe the effects in terms of molecular change. III (SC 400)

Read a thermometer to the nearest degree in either °F or °C. II (MA 375)

Identify the boiling and freezing points of water on both the Fahrenheit scale and the centigrade scale. I (MA 380)

INTERMEDIATE

Demonstrate the boiling points of various water solutions. III (MA 375)

Using the terms *expand* or *contract,* describe the state to which matter changes when heat energy is added or taken away. II

Given two states of matter, tell whether heat must be added or taken away to go from the first to the second state. Name the process involved. I

Given a description or illustration of a change of state of a liquid, explain whether the temperature of the substance was at the freezing point or the boiling point. II

Conduct an experiment to demonstrate the cause-and-effect relationship between temperature and the time it takes for a substance to dissolve in water. Use the following steps. III (SC 400)

1. Hypothesis (guess of results based on previous observation and knowledge)
2. Design (steps you will take, material you will use)
3. Record of observations
4. Conclusions

Describe how heat affects the amount of solid substance that will dissolve in water. II

Given two states of matter, explain what occurs when heat is added or taken away. Explain what has happened to the molecules between the first and second state and give the name of the process. II

Given a substance, explain the effect of heat on the volume of the substance and on the speed of the molecular action or motion. II (MA 420)

Explain the difference between the scientific definitions of *heat* and of *temperature.* Use these terms correctly in a sentence. II (MA 385)

Define *conduction, convection,* and *radiation.* I

Explain the operation of the following devices in response to temperature changes: *thermostat, thermometer, thermocouple.* II (MA 375)

INTERMEDIATE

SC 300 Show your understanding of physical and chemical properties and changes. II (SC 400)

Given a description of a physical or chemical change, conclude the effect of a given manipulated variable on that change. II

Given a series of situations in which change has taken place, describe the physical changes and the chemical changes. II

Given a chemical change, suggest variables that could affect the change. II

Given a list of specific properties of a substance, classify each property as physical or chemical. II (SC 395)

Given the name of a metal and/or a description of its properties, explain why it could or could not be used for a given purpose. II

Given the name of a gas and/or a description of its properties, explain why it could or could not be used for a given purpose. II

SC 305 Demonstrate your ability to combine concepts, principles, and generalizations by designing an experiment that demonstrates three examples of chemical change and by explaining the chemical changes that take place. V (SC 400)

Design, set up, and perform an experiment that will demonstrate that there is a 2:1 ratio of hydrogen to oxygen in water. V (MA 385)

Recognize the correct process or a step in a process to make an impure water supply potable. II

Describe several ways in which hard water can be made soft. Explain why soft water is more desirable for home use than hard water. II

INTERMEDIATE

Given a description of the process of soap making, bleaching, or fermentation, explain the function of the ingredients. Describe the products that result from each process. II

Given a description of a fire that involves any of the following combustible materials, identify what method(s) should be used and what method(s) should not be used to extinguish the fire: (1) wood, (2) electrical wiring, (3) oil, (4) fat, (5) cloth. I

Set up and conduct an experiment to demonstrate the removal of tarnish on silver objects. III (SC 400)

Tell what first-aid measures should be taken when a specified poisonous substance is swallowed. I

When performing an experiment, recognize and record signs of chemical change. II (SC 390)

SC 310 Show your understanding of an internal-combustion engine in terms of potential, kinetic, electrical, chemical, and mechanical energy. II

Given drawings that show movement of air or water molecules, recognize which illustrates the greatest production of kinetic energy. II

Given a description of machine activities that show different forms of energy (mechanical, chemical, or electrical), match each machine activity with the form of energy that it uses or produces. I

Given a description of an internal combustion engine, recognize where potential, kinetic, chemical, and mechanical energy is being used or produced. II

SC 315 Given a simple machine, show that you can demonstrate its mechanical advantages. III

Match examples of the following simple machines with ways in which they make work easier: (1) inclined plane, (2) fixed pulley, (3) wheel and axle, (4) level, (5) wedge, and (6) screw. I

INTERMEDIATE

Given drawings of levers, recognize the fulcrum, the load, and the best point to apply effort. II (MA 420)

Demonstrate the difference between the values of a fixed pulley and of a block and tackle as simple machines. III

Demonstrate relationships between effort applied and amount of work done in experimental situations using simple machines. III

Design a simple tool that will help you perform a task at school or at home. V

Given descriptions or illustrations of examples of levers, classify each as an example of a first-, second-, or third-class lever. II

Given any two of the following three variables, solve for the unknown: (1) resistance, (2) force, (3) actual mechanical advantage. II (MA 420)

Given the clockwise and counterclockwise moments or the forces and distances needed to calculate the moments of a lever (first-, second-, or third-class), apply the Law of Moments to state the rotation direction of the lever. III (MA 420)

Given seesaw word problems that include any three of the following, apply the appropriate principle and solve the problem: (1) distance to the load, (2) distance to the effort, (3) amount of load, (4) amount of effort. III (MA 420)

Given the amounts of force required to move a load and the distance of the load from the fulcrum for a first- and a second-class lever, construct a graph for each. Given the amount of force required to move a load and the distance of the force from the fulcrum for a third-class lever, construct a graph. III (MA 340)

Given a word problem containing a description of a task to be accomplished by using a lever, predict whether the task can be done. III

INTERMEDIATE

SC 320 Demonstrate your ability to combine concepts, principles, and generalizations about Newton's basic laws by designing a simple experiment that illustrates their application. Develop a hypothesis, test it with variables, draw conclusions, and make generalizations. V (SC 400)

Given a series of everyday activities, recognize those that are dependent upon gravitational force. II

Predict how the following factors affect the movement of objects: (1) forces, (2) friction, (3) unbalanced forces. III

Design a simple experiment that demonstrates the application of Newton's First Law of Motion (Law of Inertia). V

Predict which of several objects will accelerate most when given the mass of the objects and the size and direction of the force applied. III (MA 420)

Match each of the following terms with its correct definition: *motion, friction, mass.* I

Given a definition or example of speed, acceleration, velocity, inertia, or momentum, match the proper term to the definition or example. I

Given a description of a commonplace situation such as the sudden braking of a car, explain how Newton's laws of motion are illustrated. II

Explain how the gravitational force between two masses is affected by changes in the masses or by changes in the distance between the masses. Solve related problems. III (MA 420)

SC 330 Demonstrate your ability to combine concepts, principles, and generalizations by producing an electric motor or transformer, correctly wiring a model. Explain the model in terms of (1) watts, (2) voltage, (3) resistance, (4) kilowatt-hours, and (5) electron movement. V (SC 400)

Given a description or diagram of a circuit and using the term *open circuit* or *closed circuit,* describe the circuit and tell whether the circuit is on or off. II

INTERMEDIATE

Name the electrical component represented by a given symbol and tell one function of the component: (1) battery or cells, (2) switch, (3) or resistance. I

Demonstrate series circuits and parallel circuits by using the appropriate equipment and explaining the demonstration. III

Match a given definition with one of the following terms: *volt, ampere, ohm, watt.* I

Given Ohm's Law (amperage = voltage/resistance) and values for two of the variables, solve for the third variable. III (MA 420)

Find the kilowatt-hours used when given the time and the amount of electrical power consumed. III (MA 430)

Given a description of a hazardous situation involving electricity in the home, explain what should be done to remedy the situation. II

Given a description of the change of one form of energy into electrical energy, describe the original form of energy as chemical, mechanical, light, or heat energy. II

Given a description of the results of an experiment designed to determine the electrical conductivity of a material such as paper, water, or copper, classify the material as a conductor or as a nonconductor (insulator). II

Explain the behavior of conductors, insulators, and semiconductors in terms of electron movement and be able to give examples of each. II

Given a diagram of a dry cell or a voltaic cell, recognize the parts and their functions. Explain the flow of electricity through the cell and in a circuit. II

Match each of the following electronic components with its symbol and explain the function of each component: (1) diode, (2) triode, (3) capacitor, (4) resistor, (5) transistor, and (6) coil. II

INTERMEDIATE

Given examples of objects that produce current electricity, recognize the method used to produce electricity as either magnetic or chemical. II

Locate and identify the parts (core, coil, source) of an electromagnet when given a description or diagram of one. I

SC 335 Show your understanding of relationships between mass, volume, and density. II (MA 420)

Tell the difference between the operational definitions of *weight* and *mass.* I

Given the formula l × w × h, find the volume of a regular solid such as a rectangular prism, using the basic metric unit of volume, cubic centimeter. II

Given information on the mass and volume of various objects, describe how mass, volume, and density are related. II

SC 340 Show that you can demonstrate the relationship between magnetic force and electricity. III (SC 400)

Given a group of objects and a magnet, predict which of the objects are magnetic and which are nonmagnetic. Test your predictions in experimental procedures. III

Given two marked bar magnets, recognize the poles that attract each other and those that repel each other. II

Given a magnet, demonstrate the pattern of its lines of force. III

Given a magnet and a group of materials such as paper, cardboard, plastic, glass, or tin, demonstrate which materials are magnetically transparent. III

Demonstrate the difference between magnetic materials that are permanent and those that are temporary. III

Given a diagram or drawing of a magnetic field, locate the strongest and weakest lines of force in the magnetic field. I

Tell the difference between the North Geographic Pole and the North Magnetic Pole. I

Explain magnetism in terms of electron spinning and domains. II

Using a map showing lines of declination, find the magnetic declination of a point on the earth. III (SS 335, MA 420)

Given a description of an experiment, apply the magnetic-inverse-square law to explain or predict the results of the experiment. III (MA 420)

Apply information on the structure of the atom to explain static electricity. III

Explain how attraction and repulsion between charged objects are related to the kinds of electrical charges on the objects. II

Explain how the processes of induction and electron transfer are used to develop static charges on objects. II

Describe some variables that affect experiments on static electricity and explain their effect. II

Demonstrate how the strength of the magnetic field produced by an electromagnet is affected by the number of turns of wire around the core. III

Make a simple electromagnet, applying the principles of electromagnetism. Demonstrate its use to a group of people. III (SC 400)

SC 345 Show that you can interpret diagrams that illustrate the principles of sound. III

Use the molecular theory and wave theory to explain how sound travels from its source (or beginning) to the person who hears it. III

Given an experiment in which different numbers of waves are produced, draw a diagram to demonstrate how the number of waves made per second (frequency) is related to the amount of force that is required to make them. III (MA 340)

INTERMEDIATE

Given an experiment and a diagram showing the results of the experiment, recognize the relationship between the amplitude (height and depth) of the waves and the force it took to make those waves. II (MA 345)

Tell what conditions are needed for making and hearing sounds. I (SC 205)

Given the number of seconds a sound takes to travel from its source to the hearer, determine the distance traveled through the air by the sound. III (MA 420)

Given a list of materials or substances that transmit sound, identify those that carry sound waves well and those that are poor conductors. I

Given a description of the surface of a material, tell whether the surface will take in sound (absorb it) or echo (reflect) it. I

Conduct an experiment that demonstrates the relationship between expended energy and volume of sound. Change the amount of energy to vary the volume of sound produced. III (SC 400, MA 345)

Recognize the relative volume of a series of sound (loudest or softest) when shown graphs picturing their amplitude or given data about the amplitude of volume. II (MA 345)

Tell how the pitch (frequency) of a sound can be raised or lowered when the length, thickness, or tension of the vibrating object is changed. I

SC 350 Demonstrate your ability to combine concepts, principles, and generalizations by designing and presenting a demonstration of the nature and behavior of light. V

Tell how light and the parts of your eye interact to produce an image. I (SC 205)

Recognize which one of the three most common theories about the nature of light is demonstrated in examples of the way light travels. II

When you are given information about the roughness or smoothness of some objects, recognize which objects will reflect light in a scattered way and which will reflect it in a regular way. II

Recognize whether substances or objects with different surface textures and colors will reflect most of the light that falls on them or will absorb it. II

Design an experiment to show whether substances or objects with different surface textures and colors reflect or absorb most of the light that falls on them. V (SC 400)

Tell whether certain objects are transparent, translucent, or opaque. I (SC 395)

Predict the angle at which light will be reflected from a surface when given the angle at which that light strikes that surface. III (MA 420)

Recognize diagrams that correctly illustrate how white light is bent (refracted) as it passes through (1) concave and convex lenses, (2) prisms, and (3) water. II

Predict the kinds of images that will be made by convex lenses and the kinds made by concave lenses. III

SC 355 Show your understanding of the processes by which nuclear energy is produced. II

Given a description of an atom before and after a nuclear process has occurred, explain whether the atom went through (1) natural radioactive decay, (2) artificial radioactive decay (fission), or (3) fusion. II

Identify the beneficial (e.g., treatment of cancer) and the detrimental (e.g., radioactive fallout) aspects of nuclear energy. I

SC 360 Show that you can predict possible uses for computers. Explain your predictions in as much detail as possible. III (MA 335)

Define the following terms with reference to computers: *Program, data, bit, memory, printout, card, nanosecond, binary, analog, digital, disc.* I

Demonstrate how numbers written in base ten can be stored in computers as base-two (binary) units. III (MA 325)

Describe the three main parts of a computer, including (1) input, (2) central processor (control unit, arithmetic unit, and memory unit), and (3) output. II (MA 335)

Identify how computers have been used in at least two of the following areas: (1) government, (2) police work, (3) education, (4) transportation, (5) space exploration, (6) communications, (7) business, and (8) cybernetics. I (SS 250)

Discuss the use of computers in modern society in relation to the ways in which the computer might interfere with personal freedom and to the ways in which man's use of the computer might add to personal freedom. III (SS 330)

earth science

SC 365 Show your understanding of the observational data used by meteorologists in predicting weather. II (SS 340)

Tell the difference between weather and climate. Tell what atmospheric conditions are characteristic of each. I

Given drawings or descriptions of these cloud formations, identify basic cloud types: (1) cumulus, (2) cirrus, and (3) stratus. I

Match the different forms of precipitation with a description of how each is formed: (1) rain, (2) sleet, (3) hail, and (4) snow. I

Recognize the four kinds of weather fronts when given a description or an example of each: (1) warm, (2) cold, (3) stationary, and (4) occluded. II

Recognize the definitions of destructive forces of weather when given a description or diagram of each storm: (1) thunderstorm, (2) cyclone, (3) typhoon, (4) hurricane, and (5) tornado. II

Record your observations of elements of weather for a period of two weeks. Record reports from the weather bureau for any information you cannot observe yourself. II

science inquiry skills

SC 370 Demonstrate your ability to combine concepts, principles, and generalizations by designing an experiment in which these principles of learning are demonstrated: (1) learned and unlearned behavior, (2) memorization, (3) forgetting, and (4) relearning. Use the following procedures in the experiments. V

1. Formulate a hypothesis based on observations.
2. Organize your experiment with variables.
3. Draw conclusions and make generalizations.
4. Write a formal report of your findings.

Demonstrate the difference (discriminate) between a stimulus and a response in a given situation. III

In a given experiment that involves stimulus and response in living things, demonstrate the variables that are controlled (kept the same) and the ones that are changed. III

Given a list of ordinary, everyday acts performed by animals and human beings, recognize the difference between actions that are learned and actions that are not learned (reflex). II

Recognize from several groups of words or numbers one group that would probably be most easily memorized. Explain the reason why the group you selected is the easiest to remember. II

Given a list of things present in a place of study, explain the difference between those that will not prevent learning and those that will. II

Given an experiment on practice and memorization, recognize the variables that were controlled in the experiment. II

Explain ways in which a given variable was controlled in an experiment on practice and memorization. II

INTERMEDIATE

Explain which variables were controlled in an experiment on forgetting and relearning. II

Given a list of variables that were controlled in an experiment on practice and memorization, explain the reasons they were controlled. II

Given a simple graph on which a series of test scores has been plotted, explain the reasons the scores changed from test to test. II (MA 340)

Given different forms of graphs showing test scores, explain which forms can be compared most easily and interpret the scores. II

SC 375 Demonstrate your ability to combine concepts, principles, and generalizations by developing a plan for increasing your efficiency in achieving objectives through the use of effective study skills. V

Identify reasons for practicing good study skills. I

Explain the difference between study habits that are profitable and those that are of little help. II

Demonstrate three main study skills for reading and the important steps that make up each of them. III

Make a study guide including five ways to schedule your study time and five hints to remember when getting ready to study. III

Identify the four main skills for good listening and some of the rewards of good listening. I

Given a description of a learning situation, recognize variables that might make it easier for you to learn and variables that might slow down your rate of learning. II

Given several ways of improving a learned behavior (skill), recognize the one that would probably help you show the greatest progress in a given period of time and tell why your choice of methods is a good one for you. II

Given several ways of learning, predict which you think would lead to the best results for you. Test your prediction through experimental procedures. III

SC 380 Show your understanding of information about individual differences by describing a given number of your classmates. II

Discuss an example of an individual trait. Base your observation on case studies of four people who differ in respect to this trait. III

Based on definitions of heredity and environment, recognize whether specific traits are mainly a result of heredity or environment. II

Identify traits that can be changed easily and traits that cannot. I

SC 385 Show that you can use science equipment and supplies in the classroom including (1) simple microscope, (2) Bunsen burner, (3) chemicals, (4) test tubes and other glassware, (5) thermometers. III

SC 390 Show that you can design an experiment, formulate a hypothesis, record your procedures and observations, draw conclusions regarding the hypothesis, and report your results. III

SC 395 Show that you can use a taxonomic system in scientific classification. III

SC 400 Show that you can use scientific information to make a model or conduct an experiment that demonstrates a scientific principle. III

(Transitional Objectives for Inquiry Skills SC 385, SC 390, SC 395, SC 400 appear throughout the Intermediate Science section.)

SECONDARY

LIFE SCIENCE: BIOLOGY

SC 500 Show that you can use library resources to write a report on the distribution and characteristics of the subspecies of some animal (such as a squirrel), or plant (such as knotweed), in the United States. Suggest a hypothesis that would explain your findings. (A hypothesis is an idea stated in a way that it can be tested.) III (LA 570, SC 535)

Given an example of evidence for the theory of evolution, and an interpretation of that evidence, conclude whether this interpretation would support Darwin's theory of natural selection or Lamarck's theory of inheritance of acquired characteristics. II

Define and identify examples of the following factors characteristic of the evolutionary process that produce changes within a species: (1) stability, (2) change, (3) guiding (fertility and viability), and (4) random genetic drift. I

Given a description of the evolution of a new species, recognize the type of isolation that brought about the evolution (i.e., isolation by time, geographic isolation, ecological isolation, and behavioral isolation). II

Given a description of Mendel's experiments, recognize examples of the following. II (SC 535)
1. Dominant traits and recessive traits
2. Pure breeding and hybridization
3. P_1, F_1, F_2, F_3, . . . generation
4. Homozygous or heterozygous genotypes

Given the genotype of the parents and a list of the possible genotype and phenotype combinations, predict the probable ratios of the genotypes and phenotypes of the offspring. III

Given an example of dihybrid cross, apply the principles of segregation and independent assortment by describing the behavior of the alleles involved. III

Identify the major ideas in the chromosome theory. I

Recognize examples of how man has applied genetic experiments involving polyploid chromosomes to the development of a new species. II

Demonstrate an understanding of the gene theory of mutations by (1) distinguishing between gene and chromosomal mutation, (2) describing the biochemical nature of genes (include the general structure and composition of DNA and how the internal arrangement affects the variations), and (3) identifying abiotic conditions that have been observed to affect the biochemistry of genes. III

Given a scientific event or situation, suggest questions that would help to explain the event or situation. II (SC 855)

Given a question, the answer to which would help explain a scientific event or situation, suggest sources of information or activities that may lead to the answer. II (LA 560)

Write a hypothesis based on observations and inferences drawn from biological science. III

SC 505 Demonstrate your ability to combine concepts, principles, and generalizations by designing an experiment that involves an aquarium to show the effect of changes in temperature, light energy, dissolved gases, producers, and consumers on a living community. V (SC 855, SC 510)

Explain the flow of energy from the sun, through a living system, and back into the abiotic environment. II

Identify the roles of living organisms that act as food producers and organisms that act as first-, second-, or third-order food consumers. I

Given lists of chemical elements, identify the chemical elements commonly found in living organisms. I

Recognize how matter (water, CO_2, N_2, and calcium) moves cyclically between the nonliving world and the living world (the biosphere). II

SECONDARY

SC 510 Demonstrate your ability to combine concepts, principles, and generalizations by designing a procedure for studying the biotic forms in a pond or lake in your community. Complete the study and discuss the nature of the relationships among the life forms you observed and their relationships to their environment. V (SC 505)

Describe patterns and interrelationships that exist between producers and consumers in a pond community. II

Identify the abiotic factors of headwaters, lakes, deltas, and lower and middle reaches of streams, and name the organisms that best survive in those areas. I

Relate marine biotic forms to their abiotic environment by describing environmental conditions found in the spray, intertidal, and subtidal zones. Give examples of the types of marine organisms that could best survive in each zone. II

SC 515 Show your understanding of a taxonomic key by using a key to classify three given animals and three given plants. Describe each step you used, and end with the scientific name of each animal. III (SC 395)

Given a portion of a simple taxonomic chart, explain the relationships among the different branches. Starting anywhere on the chart, derive a description of an organism by working upward through the chart to the kingdom level. II

Given the class to which a vertebrate belongs, identify the kingdom, phylum, and class characteristics of that vertebrate. I

Describe the method by which plants are classified and scientifically named by accomplishing the following methods. II

1. Given several characteristics of a plant, recognize characteristics that are used by taxonomists to classify the plant.
2. Given the classification scheme for an organism, explain the binomial system of naming plants.

Given descriptions of the major structural characteristics and the method of reproduction for several common vascular plants, classify the following plants: (1) *Filicineae,* (2) *Gymnospermae,* (3) *Angiospermae.* II

Given descriptions of the major structural characteristics and the environmental conditions necessary for the survival of several common non-vascular plants, classify the plants into one of the following groups: (1) *mosses,* (2) *fungi,* (3) *algae,* (4) *lichens.* II

SC 520 Show that you can classify living and nonliving matter according to a taxonomic system. III (SC 395)

Identify the purpose for which the present system of biological classification was designed. Discuss advantages and disadvantages of this system. III

Given descriptions of various classes, recognize characteristics that are useful indications for classifying (1) at the species level and (2) at the subspecies level. II

Given a portion of a simple taxonomic chart, explain the relationships among the different branches. Starting anywhere on the chart, present a description of an organism by working upward through the chart to the kingdom level. III

Given the class to which a vertebrate belongs, identify the kingdom, phylum, and class characteristics of that vertebrate. I

Classify given cells into these categories: (1) plants, (2) animals, and (3) protists. Explain how you classified the cells by describing the principal cell structures that distinguish them. II

SC 525 Using a specific plant and animal, describe the mechanisms by which each obtains and produces energy and synthesizes organic compounds. II

Explain the function of enzymes in aerobic and anaerobic systems. II

Given the name of organic compounds that serve as building blocks, identify the classes of compounds that the cell can synthesize from these building blocks. I

SECONDARY

Given a description of the works of various scientists, explain how the work of each scientist is related to the total concept of photosynthesis. II

Given the generalized chemical reaction for photosynthesis, identify (1) raw materials for the reaction, (2) products of "light" and "dark" reactions, (3) plant structures involved in the reactions, and (4) environmental conditions necessary for the reactions. I

Demonstrate factors in energy production through an experimental procedure of your own. III

SC 530 Show that you can use specific examples drawn from the plant and animal kingdom to show your understanding of ways the differences in the mechanisms of mitosis and meiosis affect the nature of the offspring that result from asexual or sexual reproduction. III

Given diagrams of various stages of mitosis, identify in which phase the cell exists. I

Identify the following asexual methods of reproduction: (1) budding, (2) fission, (3) spore formation, and (4) vegetative reproduction. Include definitions, examples, and comparisons. I

Explain the difference between asexual reproduction and sexual reproduction by describing the general processes involved in each type as well as the genetic advantages and disadvantages that are characteristic of each type of reproduction. II

Identify the general sequence by which the monoploid (haploid) gametes are developed during the process of meiosis. I

Recognize the parts of the reproductive structure of mosses, ferns, and flowering plants. Describe the function of each structure, considering (1) reproductive parts of each type of plant, (2) plant structure in which meiosis occurs, and (3) sequence of the alternation of generations for each. II

Define the following terms as they are related to reproduction: (1) gamete formation, (2) self-fertilization, (3) hermaphroditism, (4) unisexual, and (5) parthenogenesis. I

SC 535 Demonstrate your ability to combine concepts, principles, and generalizations by designing an experiment with fruit flies to illustrate Mendel's laws. Complete each stage of the experiment and evaluate your results. V (SC 500, SC 855)

Given an example of evidence for the theory of evolution and interpretation of that evidence, conclude whether this interpretation supports Darwin's theory of natural selection or Lamarck's theory of inheritance of acquired characteristics. II

Discuss the factors characteristic of the evolutionary process that produce changes within a species: (1) stability, (2) change, (3) guiding (fertility and viability), and (4) random genetic drift factor. III

Discuss the factors in the evolution of a new species, emphasizing the type of isolation that brought the evolution about (i.e., isolation by time, geographic isolation, ecological isolation, and behavioral isolation). III

Given a description of Mendel's experiments, recognize examples of the following. II

1. Dominant traits and recessive traits
2. Pure breeding and hybridization
3. P_1, F_1, F_2, F_3 . . . generation
4. Homozygous or heterozygous genotypes

Given the genotype of the parents and a list of the possible genotype and phenotype combinations, predict the probable ratios of the genotypes and phenotypes of the offspring. III

Given an example of dihybrid cross, apply the principles of segregation and independent assortment by stating the behavior of the alleles involved. III

Identify the major ideas in the chromosome theory. I

Recognize examples of how man has applied genetic experiments involving polyploid chromosomes to the development of a new species. II

SECONDARY

Explain the gene theory of mutations by (1) differentiating between gene mutation and chromosomal mutation, (2) describing the biochemical nature of genes (include the general structure and composition of DNA and how the internal arrangement affects the variations), and (3) identifying abiotic conditions that have been observed to affect the biochemistry of the genes. II

SC 540 Using an example of a vascular plant and a non-vascular plant, show that you can write a description of the fate of nutrients taken into the plant and production of waste products by the plant. The structure in which each process takes place must be identified. III

Recognize the major structural parts of five samples of leaves. Explain the function served by each of these parts. II

Identify the structural characteristics of roots that perform the functions of storage, absorption, and anchorage. I

Recognize the major structural parts of five samples of stems. Explain the functions served by these parts. II

Identify the characteristics (structural and functional) of vascular and non-vascular plants. I

Identify the role of meristemic tissue and effects of chemicals (auxins, indoleacetic acid, 2,4-D) on the growth of plants. I

SC 545 Show your understanding of adaptations of muscular and skeletal systems of three selected vertebrates and three selected invertebrates that aid each organism in obtaining food. II

Identify the specific structural adaptations that enable organisms to acquire food. (Include frogs, jellyfish, snakes, protists, birds, and man.) I

Recognize how the skeletal and muscular systems of man and other common vertebrates are similar to those of arthropods (invertebrates) by (1) classifying the support structures of each exoskeletal or endoskeletal system, and (2) recognizing the predominant types of muscular tissue in each system. II

Explain a schematic representation of how food consumed by man is used for growth and the production of energy and how waste products are eliminated through the coordinated action of the digestive, respiratory, circulatory, and excretory systems. II

SC 550 Show that you can reasonably predict the fate of a mammalian embryo and the embryo of one other animal if mechanisms for protection and nourishment should break down during the vulnerable embryonic and pre-embryonic period of their development. III

Given sketches showing zygote cleavage and gastrula formation, identify (1) the ectoderm, mesoderm, and endoderm germ layers, and (2) the organ systems that can develop from each germ layer. I

Describe the embryonic development of a hydra, an earthworm, a fish, a bird, and a mammal, according to the following characteristics. II

1. Development within the body of the mother or external to the mother
2. Presence of yolk sac or placenta
3. Method by which nourishment is supplied to the embryo
4. Method by which the embryo is protected
5. Method by which oxygen is supplied to the embryo

Explain the development of the human animal by describing (1) formation of eggs and sperm, (2) sex organs involved in transporting the egg and the sperm, (3) union of egg and sperm, and (4) sequence of development from zygote through embryo through fetus to birth. II

SC 555 Show that you can relate different characteristics of microorganisms such as *Euglena* and *Chlamydomonas* to those of viruses in one case and true plants and animals in another case. III (SC 845)

Given a description of the work of such 19th-century scientists as Louis Pasteur and Robert Koch, recognize the phases of their works that would not have been possible without Leeuwenhoek's development of the microscope. II

SECONDARY

Recognize the characteristics of certain microorganisms (e.g., *Euglena* and *Chlamydomonas*) that indicate the need for a Kingdom Protista in addition to Kingdom Plantae and Kingdom Animalia. II

Collect samples of each of the following groups of protista: (1) bacteria, (2) ciliates, (3) amoebas, (4) sporozoans, (5) flagellates, and (6) slime molds. Recognize each group by observation. II

SC 560 Show that you can discuss factors that make a microorganism infectious or noninfectious to a particular host on the basis of your knowledge of the effect of environmental factors on the growth of microorganisms. III (SC 845)

Identify the similarities between the ecology of soil microorganisms and the ecology of larger animals. I

Identify the ecological relationships between microorganisms and multicellular plants in the nitrogen cycle. I

Identify ways the human body protects itself against pathogenic microorganisms. I

Given a description of a disease, classify the disease as infectious or noninfectious. If it is infectious, identify the vector, the pathogen, the host, and the method of disease transmission. II

Explain how the processes expressed in Koch's basic postulates relate to developments in the science of epidemiology. II

SC 565 Demonstrate your ability to combine concepts, principles, and generalizations about growth, production of energy, and elimination of waste products through the coordinated action of the digestive, respiratory, circulatory, and excretory systems by designing a schematic representation that shows how food consumed by man is used. V

Given a description of an experiment that demonstrates osmosis, explain how the processes used in the experiment illustrate osmosis in living cells. II

Given diagrams or slides of human or other animal cell types, identify the tissue origin (blood, nerve, muscle, etc.) of the cell. I

Given the major digestive structures of man, identify each of the following. I
1. The function of each structure
2. The function of enzymes lipase, amylase and pepsin
3. The presence or absence of comparable structures for hydra, earthworms, and frogs

Given the major respiratory structures of man, identify each of the following. I
1. The general function of each structure
2. The role of alveoli in the carbon dioxide-oxygen exchange
3. The presence or absence of comparable structures in fish, grasshoppers, and frogs

Given the major structures of the circulatory system of man, identify the following. I
1. The function of the transport structures
2. The function of the transported substances—blood and lymph and their components
3. The presence or absence of comparable structures in hydra, earthworms, and frogs

Given the major structures of the excretory system of man, identify each of the following. I
1. The general function of each structure
2. The presence and absence of comparable structures in planaria and the frog
3. The process of excretion, elimination, and secretion

SC 570 Demonstrate your ability to perceive the relationship of the behavior of a person who is threatened and then struck by an object and the resultant behavorial changes in the endocrine and nervous system. Emphasize the interrelatedness of the activities of these systems. IV

Given the major structures of the endocrine system, identify each of the following. I
1. The major functions of each structure
2. The method of hormone transfer
3. The major function of the entire endocrine system

SECONDARY

Given the major structures of the nervous system of man, do each of the following. II

1. Classify each structure as a part of the central, autonomic, or peripheral nervous system.
2. Describe nerve cells as motor (efferent), sensory (afferent), or associative (connective) nerve cells.
3. Identify axons, dendrites, cell body, neurilemma, and myelin on a neuron.
4. Describe the general functions of the medulla, cerebrum, and cerebellum.
5. Recognize examples of endocrine or nervous system activities that regulate internal bodily functions (i.e., heartbeat, body temperature, pupil dilation, blood-vessel construction, and enzyme secretion).

SC 575 Show that you can use correct terminology to describe learned and unlearned behavior of a group of animals selected by the teacher and observed for periods of time that total several hours. III (SC 370)

Identify definitions and examples of the following behaviors: (1) irritability, (2) tropism, (3) traces (taxis), and (4) positive and negative reactions to stimuli. I

Identify examples of innate behavior (reflexes and instincts), learned behavior (conditioning, trial-and-error), and reasoning in animals. I

Given a description of one of the following types of behaviors in vertebrates, tell whether the behavior is learned or unlearned. I

1. Food-getting behavior
2. Escape and/or protective behavior
3. Reproductive behavior
4. Social behavior
5. Locational behavior (territorial and home range, homing, and migration)

Identify activities that illustrate social behavior among such insects as honey bees, ants, and termites. I

Tell about an experiment using small animals to test a hypothesis related to learned behavior. II

SC 580 Demonstrate your ability to perceive relationships by drawing and analyzing your family tree or the family tree of an acquaintance. Attempt to explain the presence of three family traits according to Mendel's laws and then according to present-day knowledge of genetics, citing the scientist responsible for theories you use. IV (SC 500, SC 535)

Define and identify examples of the following genetic terms: (1) sex-linked traits, (2) crossing over, (3) nonallelic genes, (4) nondominance, (5) nondisjunction, (6) linkage, (7) multiple alleles, (8) mutations, and (9) chromosome mapping. I

Explain the gene theory of mutations by using the following procedures. II

1. Distinguish between gene mutation and chromosomal mutation.
2. Describe the biochemical nature of genes (include the general structure and composition of DNA and how the internal arrangement affects the variations).
3. Identify abiotic conditions that have been observed to affect the biochemistry of genes.

Identify the human traits such as color blindness that are believed to be associated with one or more of the following: (1) sex-linked genes, (2) nondominance, (3) nondisjunction, and (4) multiple alleles. I

Match the following scientists with their contributions to genetics: (1) Gregor Mendel, (2) Walter Sutton, (3) Calvin S. Bridges, (4) Thomas Morgan, (5) H. J. Muller, (6) James D. Watson and Francis H. Crick, (7) George Beadle and Edward Tatum, and (8) Karl Correns, Hugo de Vries, Erich Tschermak. I

SC 585 Demonstrate your ability to perceive the effect of uncontrolled population growth by conducting an experiment involving small fish, such as guppies. Report your observations graphically, analyze your results, and speculate on the significance of this experiment in regard to uncontrolled human population growth. IV (SS 540, MA 340)

Identify characteristics that describe individuals and those that describe populations. I

SECONDARY

Demonstrate changes in population densities by (1) defining *population density,* (2) identifying the major population determiners that increase and those that decrease population density, and (3) using the density formula to calculate the numerical change in a population when the effects of a specified population determiner are given. III

Using information concerning biotic (living environmental) and abiotic (physical environmental) factors, predict the effects that these factors would have on a given population. III

Given graphs or descriptions of population changes, recognize changes that show (1) the growth of a new population, (2) the irregular population fluctuation, and (3) a population cycle. II

SC 590 Make judgments involving the gains and losses derived by other living things resulting from three examples of man's ability to control his environment. Identify the enabling characteristic of man in each case. VI (SS 540)

Identify the major physiological and behavioral characteristics that distinguish man from other primates. I

Recognize examples of mutualism that contribute to, or are found in, the human culture. Consider products of domestication and cultivation. II

SC 595 After you have made an ecological analysis of five taxonomically classified plants or animals, show your understanding of the values of the taxonomical system or the ecological system to the biologist. II (SS 540)

Describe the differences between taxonomical and ecological classification systems. Explain the purpose served by each system. II

Given a description of a biotic interrelationship that exists in a specific ecological community, identify the relationship as an example of commensalism, mutualism, competition, scavenging, parasitism, or predation. I

Define the term *community succession* and identify examples of its occurrence. I

Given a description of changes in an abiotic variable (temperature and relative humidity) common to several communities, describe how these abiotic changes can affect members in the biotic communities. II

SC 600 Given a scientific question or problem involving biology, demonstrate your ability to combine concepts, principles, and generalizations by developing relevant hypotheses that can be tested through a series of experiments. V (SC 855)

Given a scientific event or situation, suggest questions that help to explain the event or situation. II

Given a question, the answer to which would help explain a scientific event or situation, suggest sources of information or activities that may lead to an answer to the question. II

Given a possible answer to a scientific question, develop a hypothesis that can be tested that may provide an answer to the question. V

Develop a hypothesis based on observations and inferences drawn from biological science. (A hypothesis is an idea stated in a way that it can be tested.) V

PHYSICAL SCIENCE: CHEMISTRY

SC 605 Show that you can demonstrate the structure of matter (atoms, elements, compounds, isotopes, etc.) by drawing or building models. III

Given illustrations or models of different substances, identify each substance as an element, an atom, a compound, or a mixture. I

Given a model or formula for a molecule, identify the number of atoms and elements in the molecule represented. I

SECONDARY

Given a model representing a molecule of a compound, select the formula that matches the model. I

Given atomic models of isotopes of the same element, identify the parts and tell how the models differ. I

SC 610 Show that you can use the periodic table to predict the chemical and physical properties of three elements not previously discussed. Base your prediction on a knowledge of their atomic numbers. III

Locate the following families of elements on a periodic table: (1) inert gases (noble gases), (2) metals (sodium family), (3) calcium family, (4) transitional elements, (5) nitrogen family, (6) oxygen family, and (7) halogen family. I

Using the periodic table and moving horizontally and vertically, show your understanding of physical changes and chemical reactivity (1) within a family, (2) within a period, (3) family to family, and (4) period to period. II

Given a brief description of an atomic theory, match the theory with the scientist (Dalton, Thomson, Rutherford, Bohr, Schrödinger, Einstein, de Broglie) who advanced the theory. I

Given information about a particular element from the periodic chart, recognize the correct electron configuration that would represent an atom of that element. II

SC 620 Given ionic equations that represent the reactions of selected acids or bases, show that you can reasonably predict the properties of the substances and their reactions to different indicators. III

Tell whether given properties are characteristics of acids, bases, or both. I

Given the behavior of an indicator in the pH scale, tell whether a particular color indicates an acidic solution or a basic solution. I

Balance given ionic equations or empirical equations that represent the reactions of acids and/or bases. II

SECONDARY

SC 625 Given a list of twelve elements containing both metals and nonmetals, show that you can reasonably predict which elements will form chemical bonds with one another and whether these compounds are ionic or covalent. Give the formula for the most common form of combination. III

Name the conditions that are necessary for atoms to form chemical bonds (ionic and covalent). I

Given elements that react to form ionic compounds and using the periodic chart, write empirical formulas for the compounds. III

Given elements that react to form covalent molecules, use the periodic table to write molecular formulas for the molecules. III (SC 610)

SC 630 Demonstrate your ability to combine concepts, principles, and generalizations by designing an experiment that will demonstrate the differential behaviors of solutions having the same molar strength but containing either ionic or nonionic solutes. V

Given the weight in grams of a sample of a substance and using a chart or table of atomic weights, calculate the maximum amount of a 1 M aqueous solution that can be prepared. II

Given a description of an experiment in which a substance has been tested for its electrolytic properties, interpret the results of the experiment according to the Ionic Theory of Conductivity. II

Given the empirical formulas of substances that conduct electricity in a water solution, write ionic equations to represent what happens when these substances dissociate. III

Demonstrate the differences between the behavior of solutions (such as salt water) and pure substances (such as water) according to (1) time required to reach the boiling and freezing points, (2) respective temperatures at which boiling and freezing take place, and (3) respective vapor pressures. III (SC 850)

As freezing or boiling of a solution continues, predict how the properties of the solution (vapor pressure, concentration of solute, density, boiling temperature, freezing temperature) will vary. Test your predictions. III

SECONDARY

SC 635 Demonstrate your ability to perceive the relationship of nuclear equations to the decay of two isotopes (such as 131_I and 32_P). Determine the relative number of particles emitted by each nucleus after a given time period. IV

Apply the concept of half-life of radioactive isotopes to solve word problems. III

Given a nuclear reaction with all the reactants and products described except one, complete the equation for the reaction. Classify the type of reaction as (1) alpha or beta decay, (2) fusion, or (3) fission. II

Identify statements that are characteristic of fusion and fission reactions. II

SC 640 Show that you can write a paper describing how hydrocarbons may be processed in industry to yield products useful to modern man. III

Describe the processes of fractional distillation, polymerization, and cracking. Recognize illustrations of each process. II

Given examples of chemical reactions involving aromatic hydrocarbons, classify the reaction as halogenation, nitration, sulfonation, or Friedel-Crafts. II

SC 645 Given reactants and conditions for several organic reactions, show that you can reasonably predict the principal products and can identify these products by formula and name. III

Given a random list of chemical properties, identify the properties that are characteristic of organic compounds. I

Given the names and the structural and molecular formulas of organic compounds, classify the compounds as saturated, unsaturated, or aromatic hydrocarbons. II

Given the structural formula of an organic compound, (1) classify the compound according to the functional group (alcohol, aldehyde, carboxyl, amine, carbonyl), and (2) name the compound. II

Given the reactants and conditions of an organic reaction, recognize principal products and balance the equation. II

SC 650 Knowing the value for K_A of an acid and its concentration in a solution, show your understanding of reaction by calculating the pH of the solution. II

Given the equation for the reaction of an acid and a base and a table of values for K_A, explain whether reactants or products are favored. II

Given the volume and concentration of a strong acid and a strong base, calculate the hydrogen ion and hydroxide ion concentration for the acid-base solution. II

SC 655 From a description of the results of an experiment involving a chemical change in which one of the products is a gas, demonstrate your ability to perceive the data using chemical equations. Relate the predicted weight and volume of gas to the actual yield. IV (SC 860)

Given the formula of a compound and the atomic weights of its elements, calculate the percentage composition of the compound. II

Given the percentage composition of a compound and the atomic weights of its elements, calculate the empirical formula of the compound. II

Given the fact that one mole of any gas at standard temperature and pressure (STP) has a volume of 22.4 liters, and the density of a gas at STP, calculate the gram-molecular weight of the gas. II

Given a balanced equation and the atomic weights of the elements involved, calculate the weight of a reactant required to produce a known amount of a product, or the weight of a product produced by a known amount of a reactant. II

Using the quantity of 11.4 liters/mole, calculate the mass of a substance needed to produce a given volume of a gas (at STP) or the volume of a gas produced by a given mass of a substance. II

Given a balanced equation of reacting gases at STP, calculate the volume of a reactant (or product) when the volume of a product (or reactant) is known. II

SECONDARY

SC 660 Demonstrate your ability to combine concepts, principles, and generalizations by developing a scheme of analysis for identifying the composition of an unknown solution or solid. Use a variety of laboratory tests, flame tests, precipitation, borax bead test, blowpipe tests (cobalt nitrate tests), and paper chromatography. Identify the unknown. V (SC 855)

Perform chemical tests on several known solutions or solids and one unknown solution or solid to identify their composition. III

Given a scheme of analysis, determine the composition of an unknown solution or solid. IV

SC 665 Show that you can discuss how the chemical and physical characteristics of carbohydrates and lipids, proteins, and nucleic acids make them particularly well-suited as sources of energy, enzymes, and hereditary material in the living cell. III

Recognize a simple sugar, a starch, a lipid, and a protein, given the structural formula and chemical characteristics for each form. II

Given the building materials and energy sources available to the cell, predict changes in cell metabolism. III

Given the properties (composition, acid-base characteristics, structure) of enzymes, explain how the enzymes catalyze chemical reactions in the cell. II

Given the chemical makeup of hereditary material, describe its role in protein synthesis, its method of production, and mechanisms of its transmission from one generation to another. II

SC 670 Show that you can design an experiment in which you have to demonstrate how different forms of energy (including heat energy) can be produced in a chemical reaction. V (SC 845)

Given the equations for endothermic or exothermic reactions and a table of heats of reaction between elements, calculate the amount of heat lost or gained in forming the product. II

Describe the relationship between chemical and mechanical forms of energy. II

Explain how the Law of Conservation of Energy applies to the production of energy in chemical reactions. II

Describe the difference in the relative amounts of energy involved in a physical change, a chemical change, and a nuclear change. II

SC 675 Using the table of oxidation potentials, show that you can reasonably predict reaction of three pairs of substances with one another. Explain the bases for your predictions. III (SC 860)

Explain the difference between oxidation and reduction in terms of (1) experimental chemical behavior, (2) change in oxidation number, and (3) half-reaction equations. II

Given the reactants of an electrolytic process, go through the following procedures. III

1. Write half-cell equations for those substances oxidized and tell why oxidation has occurred.
2. Write half-cell equations for the substances reduced and tell why reduction has occurred.
3. Write the products and balance the equation.

Given a redox equation, go through the following procedures. III

1. Demonstrate how conservation of charge and matter is maintained, using half-reactions.
2. Balance the equation.
3. Use the table of oxidation potentials (E^0) to predict whether or not the reaction will take place spontaneously.
4. Compute the E^0 total for the redox reactions.

Write half-cell equations to describe desirable and undesirable redox reactions. III

Explain how Faraday's experiments in electrochemistry gave further evidence for Dalton's atomic theory. II

SC 680 Show that you can reasonably predict how changes in (1) pressure, (2) temperature, (3) concentration of reactants, and (4) addition of a catalyst would affect the rate of a reaction and the point of equilibrium for that reaction. III (SC 850)

Given the nature of reactants, the concentration of reactants, the temperature change, and the addition of a catalyst, describe how each condition affects the rate of a chemical reaction. II

SECONDARY

Given a closed equilibrium system, predict how the system would shift because of changes in (1) pressure, (2) temperature, or (3) concentration. III

Given two solutions of known molarity and a table of solubility products, predict whether a precipitate will form when two solutions are mixed. III

Given an equilibrium system, describe how the heat content and the random distribution of the reactants and products vary. II

SC 685 Show your understanding of relationships of properties of colloidal particles to properties of macromolecules such as proteins that are of colloidal size. II

Recognize the chemical and physical properties of colloids that account for the behavior and practical application of colloids. II

Recognize which particles found in living things are of colloidal size. II

SC 690 Demonstrate your ability to perceive the difference between energy changes associated with chemical reactions and energy changes associated with physical changes. IV

Given equations for chemical reactions, explain whether the reactions are endothermic or exothermic. II

Classify described substances as elements, compounds, or mixtures. II

Describe phase changes associated with the gain or loss of energy. II

SC 695 Show that you can discuss the gas laws in terms of the amount of kinetic energy possessed by the molecules of gaseous substances. III

Express the relationship between the volume and the pressure of a confined gas, and solve related problems. II

Express the relationship between the volume of a confined gas and its absolute temperature, and solve related problems. II

Given Avogadro's number, the periodic table, and the mass of a given gas, calculate the number of moles and molecules contained in that gas. II

Interpret a graph illustrating changes in the amount of kinetic energy possessed by the molecules of a gaseous substance at different temperatures. II

SC 700 Demonstrate your ability to combine concepts, principles, and generalizations by designing and performing an experiment concerning a problem in chemistry that you have defined. Write a complete laboratory report. V (SC 855)

Make an inference from a set of observations drawn from chemistry. IV

From a list of observations drawn from chemistry, recognize the observations that support a given inference. II

Recognize observations and inferences from a mixed list of them drawn from chemistry. II

Represent chemistry data in a table and a graph. II

Translate chemistry data from a graph into a table. II

From a list of statements, recognize statements that appear to originate from a graph about chemistry. II

Explain the way two variables and a graph of chemical data are related. II (SC 860)

Given a list of safety rules and information about laboratory techniques in wearing safety equipment, locating and using fire extinguishers, using a first-aid kit, handling chemicals, mixing acid solutions, and cleaning up, demonstrate that you can apply the rules and information during your investigations and experiments and that you understand their purposes. III (SC 845)

SECONDARY

PHYSICAL SCIENCE: PHYSICS

SC 705 Given a brief history of the development of a physical law, show your understanding of the law's history by indicating the period of time that the law was first a hypothesis, the period that the hypothesis became a theory, and the period that the theory became a law. II

Differentiate between fact and theory. III

Define *hypothesis, theory,* and *law.* I

SC 710 Show that you can make measurements and calculations with respect to time, distance, area, and volume as required in word problems and express results in scientific notation. III (MA 420, MA 600)

Using scientific (exponential) notation, solve given word problems that involve measurements of time and require calculations and/or experiments. III

Solve given word problems that involve measurements of distance, area, and volume and require calculations and/or experiments. Express results in significant figures. III

SC 715 Demonstrate your ability to combine concepts, principles, and generalizations by developing mathematical functions to express relationships in physics and applying the equations in solving word problems. V (MA 595, MA 695)

Write an equation for a given mathematic relationship and apply the equation in solving word problems. III (MA 420)

Solve word problems in vector addition and multiplication of a vector by a scalar (an ordinary number) using three methods: (1) graph, (2) components, and (3) trigonometry. III

SC 720 Demonstrate your ability to combine concepts, principles, and generalizations by developing relationships among the various properties of objects moving in space. V (SC 855, MA 595)

Given a table of the positions of an object at various times, represent on graphs, position versus time, average velocity versus time, and average acceleration versus time. III

Given a graph of the position of an object moving in a line versus time, represent on a table, position versus time, velocity versus time, and acceleration versus time. III

Given a table of the positions of an object at various times, find the *x, y,* and *z* components of the average velocity between those points. III (SC 860)

From a set of component velocities or accelerations, find the resultant velocity or acceleration. III

SC 725 Show that you can demonstrate the properties of force and the ways in which properties interact. III (MA 695, MA 700)

Given a description of a force, classify the force as a vector or a scalar quantity. II

Identify three pre-Galilean concepts of force and list the empirical support for each concept. I

Given a description of three simultaneous forces acting in a plane on an object, find the *x* and *y* components of the resultant force on the object. III

Given a written description of a series of forces applied to an object of mass *M,* find its velocity in three dimensions after each force is applied. III

Develop a definition of mass, explaining the difference between inertial mass and active and passive gravitational mass, and the difference between mass and weight. V

Describe the various forces found in nature, explaining (1) the distances over which the forces act, (2) their strength, and (3) the quantities (such as mass) on which they depend. Include frictional, gravitational, electrical, magnetic, and nuclear forces. III

Calculate the gravitational forces acting between two massive bodies. III (MA 700)

SC 730 Demonstrate your ability to perceive relationships expressed in the conservation laws and to solve problems utilizing these laws. IV (MA 695, MA 700)

Given an impulse applied to a stationary mass, calculate its subsequent velocity and momentum. II

Using the law of the conservation of momentum, solve word problems concerning head-on collisions between two masses. III

Find the quantity of kinetic energy given to an object from the amount of work performed on the object. Explain the difference between work and force. III

Find the amount of potential energy stored in compressed springs and in elevated objects. III

Solve word problems involving colliding or falling bodies, using the law of conservation of energy. III

Given a description of a mechanical event such as the launching of a satellite, support an explanation of the event in terms of the laws of conservation of energy and momentum. III

SC 735 Demonstrate your ability to perceive relationships expressed in the kinetic theory of gases and to solve problems utilizing this theory. IV (MA 695, MA 700)

Solve word problems concerning the amount of heat energy in given bodies at various temperatures and problems concerning the exchange of heat between various bodies. III

Use the kinetic theory of matter to describe molecular motion of the different phases of matter. III

Describe the relationship between the molecular theory of gases and Boyle's law. Solve word problems using Boyle's law. III (SC 695)

Describe the relationship between the ideal gas law and the kinetic theory of gases. Solve word problems using the ideal gas law. III

Find the amount of positive or negative work done by a gas expanding or contracting relative to its surroundings during adiabatic and isothermal processes. III

Using Bernoulli's law, solve word problems and answer questions concerning moving fluids. III

SC 740 Show that you can demonstrate the characteristics of wave motion. III

Describe transverse and longitudinal mechanical waves in a string or spring and calculate the wave length as a function of wave velocity and frequency. III

Discuss the principles of reinforcement as applied to waves that are reflected and to waves that are refracted around objects. III

Draw and discuss diagrams illustrating the superposition principle and the interference of waves. III

SC 745 Make judgments involving the characteristics of light waves. VI

Compare the wave theory and particle theory of light. Include in your comparison (1) an application of Snell's law, (2) a discussion of the independent measurements of Foucault and Michelson to verify the wave theory, and (3) a discussion of the role of the principle of refraction in both theories. VI

Present a theory about why interference effects are not normally seen in light. Using this theory and Thomas Young's experiment, determine wave length from observed interference effects. Explain how your conclusions support the wave theory of light. IV

Given the interference pattern of a monochromatic light source, solve word problems related to the wave length of that light. III (MA 420, MA 595, MA 600)

SECONDARY

Write a paper in which you compare Huygens' wave model of light with diffraction phenomena, particularly as applied to diffraction gratings. Determine the wave length of incident light from the optical geometry of a transmission grating. VI (LA 570)

SC 750 Demonstrate your ability to perceive relationships among the principles of optics. IV (SC 860)

Experimentally support the two laws of reflection, and solve related word problems. III

Geometrically analyze image formation by plane mirrors and by spherical mirrors. Your analysis should include a discussion of curved-mirror terminology and a comparison of real and virtual image formation. IV (MA 630, MA 640)

Draw ray diagrams of image formation by concave mirrors for several object positions. Discuss the relationship between mirror focal length and relative object-image position for each case. Solve related word problems. III (MA 640)

Using Snell's law and the theory of index of refraction, solve word problems related to the passage of a light ray through an interface between any two media. When appropriate, apply the theory of reversibility. III

Draw principal ray diagrams of image formation by converging lenses and diverging lenses. Discuss the difference between image formation by lenses and image formation by spherical mirrors. III

Based on the concept of the variation of index of refraction with color, explain sunlight dispersion by a prism. Utilize a refractive diagram of a prism in your explanation. II

SC 755 Demonstrate your ability to perceive relationships expressed in the quantum theory of light by solving problems utilizing this theory. IV (MA 695, MA 700)

Explain the development of the electromagnetic theory of light from Faraday to Hertz. Given the general character of electromagnetic radiations, classify the radiations in the eight major regions of the electromagnetic spectrum. II

Explain the three laws of photoelectric emission. Describe to what extent a wave model of light is successful in explaining these laws. II

Recognize the definition of the quantities in Einstein's photoelectric equation. Describe the significance of the photoelectric effect and the assumptions of Planck. II

Given Planck's relationship describing the energy of a photon radiated at frequency f from some source and Einstein's equation for mass-energy equivalency, develop an equation for the momentum associated with that photon in terms of its wave length. V

SC 760 Demonstrate your ability to perceive electric charges and electric current and to analyze relationships between them under various conditions. IV

Given a description of two kinds of electric charges and the forces between them, explain how these forces can be understood in terms of charged particles in atoms. II

Given a description of the behavior of an electroscope, explain the electrostatic induction phenomenon in terms of charged particles in atoms. II

Explain how the electroscope can be refined and used for accurate quantitative measurements. II

Using a battery as an example of a device for separating electrical charges, draw a diagram and describe how this charge separation can result in an electric current. III

Define *electric current.* I

Prepare a table of electrical conductivity according to state, temperature, and material. III

Using Coulomb's law, solve problems involving electrical forces between two charges. III

Use Millikan's oil-drop experiment as a basis for measuring the constant of proportionality in Coulomb's law. III

SECONDARY

Calculate the mass of an electron or a proton when given the speed attained by either particle in traversing a known distance. III (MA 695, MA 700)

Using a qualitative definition of electric current in terms of moving elementary charges, describe how currents can be measured by electrolysis. II

Design an experiment to verify the following assumptions by measuring the kinetic energy of a beam of moving charges. V (SC 850)
1. All elementary charges are the same.
2. The force on a moving charge is independent of its speed.

Describe electric field and potential difference in terms of interactions between elementary charged particles. II

Using the concepts of electric field and potential difference, define open and closed circuits and describe methods of measuring potential differences. II

Describe electric circuits from the viewpoint of kinetic energy and charged particles. Solve problems using Ohm's law. III (MA 420)

SC 765 Demonstrate your ability to perceive relationships between magnetic fields and the currents producing them. IV

Describe the sources and nature of magnetic fields and the relationship of the magnetic field strength to the current producing the field. II

For a current in a magnetic field, calculate the direction of the force exerted on the current relative to the direction of the current and of the magnetic field. Relate the magnitude of the magnetic force to the magnitude, force field, and force vector of the electric current. III

Assuming that the force on a current is the sum of the forces on the elementary particles of which the current is composed, apply the scientific principle involved to development of an expression for the force exerted by a magnetic field on a moving charged particle. III

Describe how masses of charged particles can be measured by accelerating the masses to a known energy with a magnetic field perpendicular to their velocity. Describe how interacting magnetic and electric fields can be used to identify fast-moving charged particles. II

Use the concept of circulation of the magnetic field around the current producing the field to describe the magnetic field at a distance *r* from a long straight wire. Explain how Ampere's circuital law applies to this situation. II

By experimentation, find the constant in the circulation law and state complete equations for the magnetic field produced by various current configurations. III (SC 860)

SC 770 Show your understanding of electromagnetic induction by demonstrating its principles. III (SC 400)

Recognize how Faraday's experiments dealing with a loop moving through a magnetic field contributed to the concept of magnetic flux. II

Explain the relationship existing between the induced EMF in a conductor and the rate of change of the magnetic flux. II

Describe how an electric field can be induced by a changing magnetic flux. Describe how the principles of electricity and magnetism make possible the prediction that electric and magnetic fields can propel themselves through space. II

SC 775 Show that you can present the evidence for modern theories concerning wavelike properties of particles of matter. III

Present in an outline the experimental support for de Broglie's proposal that particles of matter have wavelike properties associated with them. III

Describe the significance of the de Broglie relation by explaining the behavior of a particle of small kinetic energy moving in or near an atom. II

Recognize three major characteristics of subatomic particles that enable man to detect the presence of these particles. Describe the operation of instruments or devices that can be used to detect these particles. II

Identify the differences between Van de Graaff generators, circular accelerators, and linear accelerators in relation to (1) types of particles accelerated, (2) particle energies attainable, (3) operation, and (4) current use. I

Identify fundamental subatomic particles as baryons, mesons, or leptons. List three conservation laws that apply to the nuclear interactions of these particles. I

Express the principle of symmetry and the law of parity. Describe the connection between the two concepts. Describe the experimental failure of the theory of conservation of parity. II

SC 780 Demonstrate your ability to perceive relationships of evidence and experiments to the concepts of quantum systems and quantum mechanics. IV

Describe the Franck-Hertz experiment and its significance in predicting photon spectra that should arise when an atom changes its energy state. II

Given an energy-level diagram for an atom of mercury, predict the spectral lines that appear when the atom is bombarded with electrons. III

Describe the numerical results for the energy levels of atomic hydrogen. Include a comparison of the basic results of Balmer and Rydberg. II

Using Newton's law ($F = ma$) and the de Broglie hypothesis ($\lambda = h/mv$), find the energy-level relationship for atomic hydrogen. Relate the derivation to the wave mechanics of a "particle in a box." IV (MA 695, MA 700)

Explain how Franck and Hertz's electron bombardment experiment revealed the presence of atomic energy levels. II

List reasons why the wave properties of atoms might be a possible explanation for discrete energy levels. II

Identify the four "quantum numbers" of an electron and explain how they, with the help of the exclusion principle, make it possible to determine the electron configuration in any atom. II

Identify examples of the contributions of Heisenberg, Franck, Hertz, Pauli, de Broglie, Planck, and Schrödinger to the field of quantum physics. I

SC 785 Show that you can write and present a paper on an area in which physics is currently being widely employed and in which its frontiers are being expanded. Include a discussion of prospects for future development. III (LA 570)

List laws from physics that are being widely used in research and industry. I

Describe the research being conducted in an industrial plant or in a research organization in your section of the country. II

Find information about the work being done in an area of physics today. III

earth science

SC 790 Show that you can discuss the relative positions of the various astronomical bodies in the universe. Describe the nature of forces among the astronomical bodies. III

Identify the relative positions of the following astronomical bodies in the universe: (1) stars, (2) planets, (3) our solar system, (4) our galaxy, (5) asteroids, (6) meteoroids, and (7) comets. I

Draw a diagram representing the order of the planets from the sun, and be able to discuss the relative distances of the planets. III

Given a description of movements in space or the gravitational attraction between two bodies, use the formula for gravity $F_g = G M_1 \times M_2/d^2$ as a basis for formulating a general mathematical interpretation. III (MA 420)

SECONDARY

Explain how knowledge of gravitational force was used to predict (1) the presence of Neptune and Pluto before they were discovered and (2) the presence of large quantities of light gases on the major planets. II

SC 795 Show your understanding of the origin and nature of rocks of the earth. II

Describe the relationships of (1) temperature, (2) pressure, and/or (3) amount of water or ions free to move in the rock, to the formation of metamorphic rock from described parent-rock environments. Include contact and regional metamorphism. II

Classify igneous, sedimentary, and metamorphic rocks when given samples, descriptions, or sources. II

Given information derived from igneous rocks (texture, grain size, color, or mineral content), draw conclusions about (1) relative depth under the surface where the rock was formed, (2) whether the rock was originally molten rock, and (3) conditions under which the rock would have been formed. II

SC 800 Show your understanding of composition of the earth, conditions under which various materials were formed, and ways and means of testing the materials that make up the earth. II

Define the terms *atoms, isotopes, ions, molecules, elements,* and *compounds,* and explain how each is related to minerals and rocks. II

Given several conditions necessary for the formation of certain minerals and a list of minerals found in a particular area, select the environmental conditions that probably existed in that particular area. II

Describe the chemical composition of the earth's three spheres: lithosphere, hydrosphere, and atmosphere. II

Given a description of the manner in which a certain rock was formed, classify the rock as metamorphic, sedimentary, or igneous. II

Identify definitions of *fracture, cleavage, streak, hardness, texture,* and *luster.* Tell what laboratory or field procedures are used to determine these properties. Interpret the results of laboratory tests. II

SC 805 Show that you can discuss how and why changes occur in the features of the earth. III (SS 635)

Given a description or illustration of a change in a feature of the earth, predict the change agent that most likely produced the alteration. Change agents include wind, water, volcanoes, meteorites, glaciers, landslides, and waves. III (SS 635)

Given an experiment showing changes occurring across the interfaces of common objects, predict the following conditions. I (SC 860)

1. What the changes are and where they occur
2. Which variables affect the rate (speed) at which these changes occur
3. How the experiment could be similar to natural changes on the earth's surfaces

Given examples of various earth change agents, classify the agent as either natural or man-made. II

Given a description of weathered materials (natural or man-made) and a description of the original material, select the appropriate causes of such weathering. II

Relate the development of mature soils from unweathered rock to (1) the passing of time, (2) movement of minerals and organic colloids, and (3) depth of transformation. II

Given an erosional agent (water, wind, ice), relate the effects of gravity and kinetic energy to the erosion of different types of material. II

Given the rate of current flow and the size of various particles being transported, predict the settling rates and graded bedding that would result. III (MA 420)

Differentiate between relevant and irrelevant facts associated with a hypothesis explaining geosyncline formation. III

SECONDARY

Given a diagram or description of a geosyncline (1) identify the locations of various-sized sedimentary rocks, (2) name the type of deformation if present (anticline or syncline), and (3) interpret possible means of the geosyncline deformation. II

Interpret continental profile maps, graphs, or illustrations showing depth and/or region relationships of (1) volcanic chains, (2) deep-sea trenches, (3) mountains, and (4) earthquake activity. II (SS 635)

Describe relationships between areas of earthquake activity, mountain regions, ocean trenches, island arcs, and volcanoes. II (SS 635)

SC 810 Demonstrate your ability to perceive relationships of the various factors that create weather conditions. IV (SS 640)

Relate the earth's distance from the sun to the simultaneous existence of water in the gaseous, liquid, and solid states. II

Identify how water-cycle processes of condensation, sublimation, precipitation, and melting are dependent upon energy transfer. I

Identify appropriate cloud formations necessary to produce the following forms of precipitation: (1) rain, (2) hail, (3) sleet, and (4) snow. I

Tell how air masses are created and how they supply the energy needed for development of cyclones along a polar front. I

On an outline map of the world, identify the following major climatic regions: (1) polar ice cap, (2) tundra (polar wet), (3) taiga (subpolar wet), (4) humid continental, (5) humid subtropical, (6) Marine West Coast, (7) Mediterranean, (8) steppe and desert (continental dry), (9) savanna, (10) tropical (rain forest). I (SS 640)

On an outline map of Africa identify the following climatic regions: (1) Mediterranean, (2) semiarid (steppe), (3) arid (desert), (4) tropical wet and dry (savanna), (5) tropical wet (rain forest), (6) humid subtropical. I (SS 635)

Predict weather conditions from data relating to air temperature, pressure, and wind. III (SS 640)

On an outline map of Africa that identifies circulation patterns, predict the climatic characteristics of the following patterns: (1) January winds, (2) July winds, and (3) ocean currents. III (SS 640)

SC 815 Show your understanding of the various ways in which water interacts with the land. II (SS 650)

Identify the various forms in which moisture reaches the earth and the ways in which this moisture is stored. I

Interpret relationship of soil particle size to the formation of capillary and gravity water. Discuss (1) porosity, (2) water retention, and (3) permeability. II

Define evapotranspiration rate, and identify three methods that can be used to measure it. I

Given the potential evapotranspiration rate (PE) and the amount of moisture supplied to a geographic region by precipitation, suggest (1) the water deficiency or surplus, and (2) the amount of vegetation in that area. II

Given the necessary data and a graph that shows the water budget for a geographic region, indicate three factors that affect the water budget. III

SC 820 Show your understanding of the nature of the sea-air interface. II (SS 650)

Given discrepancies in salinity content within the hydrological cycle, identify the possible sources (causes) of such changes. I

Identify the physical and chemical properties of the sea or atmosphere that affect matter and energy transfer across the sea-air interface. I

Relate the importance of solar energy to ocean wave and current formation. II

SC 825 Given a description of environments and using biome maps and climatogram information, demonstrate your ability to perceive the probable distribution of living things. IV (SS 650)

SECONDARY

Given a description of an environment, recognize which conditions are the major determiners of the types of organisms that can survive in that environment. II

From biome maps and climatogram information, recognize the major abiotic environmental factors that determine a specific biome type. II

Identify the general biotic conditions that are common to most biomes. I

Determine the methods that man has used or could use to transform a specific biome, making the biome more adaptable to man's way of life. IV

Conduct an experiment to test variables you have selected that affect the rate of decomposition of organic materials. III

SC 830 Show that you can discuss a description of work done by a group of scientists on sediment dating and radioactive clock methods of dating. Consider how their results clarify the mechanisms involved in the decline of one group of animals and the increase in another group of animals. III

Given the general results of work by scientists, infer whether the work contributes to the geologic record of life in the past or to a theory explaining the origin of life. II

Describe sediment dating and radioactive clock methods of dating fossils. II

1. An adequate description of the sediment method must mention when sediment dating is appropriate, the general age of the bottom layer in comparison to other layers in the same strata, and why sediment layers are compared to the layers in other locations.
2. An adequate description of the radioactive clock method must mention one radioactive isotope used and the stable isotope formed, what half-life means in terms of the given isotope, and how this method helps to date sedimentary rocks.

Given a chart that illustrates evolutionary relationships of organisms, recognize the common ancestors of different organisms. II

Identify the factors that eventually led to a decline in the dominance of amphibians and reptiles and to an increase in the dominance of mammals. I

SC 835 Show that you can reasonably predict the success of various methods of preventing and controlling pollution. III (SS 540)

Identify the major sources of environmental pollution. I

Describe the effect of specific chemical pollutants on living and nonliving matter in the environment. II

SCIENCE INQUIRY SKILLS

SC 840 Show that you can use the metric system of measurement by applying the system in all scientific experiments performed during the year. III

Identify the basic metric unit that is used for measuring each of the following: (1) length, (2) weight, (3) volume, and (4) temperature. I

Define each of the prefixes used to indicate different units of measure in the metric system (milli-, centi-, deci- and kilo-). Given a measure of length, volume, or weight in any metric unit, convert the measure to any other metric unit of length, volume, or weight. III

Measure the length of objects in metric units to within .1 centimeter (cm). III

Measure the volume of solids and liquids in metric units to within 1 milliliter (ml). III

Calculate the volume of rectangular solids to within .1 cubic centimeter (cc). III

Measure the weight of objects in metric units to within .1 gram (gm). III

Measure temperatures to within 1°C or 1°F. III

SECONDARY

Record as many observations as possible. Record all measurements in metric system terms. III

Given a number less than 100,000, express the number to three significant figures. Given an extremely large or small number, express it in scientific notation (exponential notation). Given the range of uncertainty ($\pm$ principle) of an instrument and a reading from that instrument, write a corrected expression for that reading. II

SC 845 In the laboratory show that you can use the equipment by (1) correctly identifying and reproducing in a drawing three structures of microscopic size, and (2) using the gas burner and filtering system properly. III

Locate on a diagram the following parts of a compound microscope: (1) base, (2) arm, (3) stage, (4) stage clips, (5) mirror or light, (6) objectives, (7) ocular, (8) barrel, and (9) diaphragm. Identify the function of each of these parts. Identify from a group of statements the statements that describe correct techniques for operating a compound monocular microscope. I

Locate on a diagram the following parts of a laboratory gas burner: (1) barrel, (2) collar, (3) air inlet, (4) gas inlet, (5) gas valve, and (6) base. Identify the function of each of these parts. Identify from a group of statements the statements that describe correct techniques for operating a laboratory gas burner. I

Locate on a diagram the following parts of a filtering system: (1) funnel, (2) filter paper, (3) stirring rod, (4) beaker, (5) wash bottle, (6) ring stand, (7) filtrate, (8) residue, and (9) wash. I

Explain the maintenance and operation of the compound monocular microscope. II

SC 850 Demonstrate your ability to perceive relationships in a laboratory experiment by making inferences and predictions based upon quantitative results that you have tabulated and graphed. IV

Given a statement of the observations from an experiment, classify each observation as qualitative or quantitative. II

Given the results of a laboratory procedure (experiment), record the results and display them in tabular and graphic form. II

Describe the factual information displayed in a graph. II

Explain the way two variables on a graph of biological data are related. II

Analyze and discuss results of an experiment that have been expressed graphically. IV

Accurately record observations of an experiment and draw inferences that are supported by the data. IV

Given a description of a scientific experiment, summarize the information given into a complete laboratory report including (1) title, (2) problem, (3) hypothesis, (4) procedure, (5) data, and (6) conclusion. II

SC 855 Demonstrate your ability to combine concepts, principles, and generalizations by designing and conducting an experiment to test the validity of a given hypothesis and by analyzing and reporting the results. V

Given a scientific event or situation, suggest questions that would help explain the event or situation. II

Given a question, the answer to which would help explain a scientific event or situation, suggest sources of information or activities that may lead to an answer to the question. II

Make an inference from a set of observations. IV

Develop a hypothesis based on observations and inferences. (A hypothesis is an idea stated in such a way that it can be tested.) V

Given a hypothesis that can be tested, design a laboratory procedure (experiment) that will test the hypothesis. V

SECONDARY

SC 860 Show that you can make reasonable predictions based on laboratory observations and measurements stated in a table or in graph form, using either interpolation or extrapolation. (Interpolation: predicting between two points; extrapolation: predicting beyond the last known point.) III (MA 340, 345)

Given descriptions of particular attitudes or beliefs, differentiate between attitudes or beliefs formed after scientific observation and those based upon previously formed or untested beliefs. III

Given a table or graph of the results of an experiment, (1) interpret the results, (2) make predictions based upon the results, and (3) determine whether the results support, refute, or have no bearing upon the hypothesis tested. IV

Given an example of a graph, make inferences and predictions based upon information presented in graphical form. IV

appendix

TERMINAL OBJECTIVES

LIFE SCIENCE

PRIMARY

SC 005 Show your understanding of the properties of a given plant or animal. II

SC 010 Show that you know about the functions of the ear, eye, nose, and tongue. I

SC 015 Show your understanding of the senses by classifying objects according to touch, smell, taste, sight, and sound. II

SC 020 Show your understanding of the differences in animal reproduction. II

SC 025 Show that you know about interaction of organisms with their environment. I

INTERMEDIATE

SC 200 Given a drawing of the human body, show that you know about body systems and body parts. I

SC 205 Show your understanding of the human body by matching the names of human body systems and body parts to a description of their major functions. II

SC 210 Show your understanding of basic human needs by recognizing the items necessary to maintaining a healthy existence. II

SC 215 Show your understanding of the characteristics of given organisms that are harmful to man. II

SC 220 Show that you can collect information about and discuss human diseases. III

SC 225 Show that you can collect information about and discuss the effects of tobacco, alcohol, and drugs on the human body, using reliable reports of research. III

TERMINAL OBJECTIVES

SC 230 Show that you can use selected diagrams, pictures, or models to demonstrate the adaptive powers of plants and animals. III

SC 235 Show your understanding of characteristics and functions of plant and animal cells. II

SC 240 Show that you can use scientific classifications to classify given plants and animals. III

SC 245 Demonstrate your ability to combine concepts, principles, and generalizations by designing an investigation of a biological problem that involves the use of the microscope and other tools of the modern biologist. V

SC 250 Show your understanding of the reproductive process in plants, insects, and animals. II

SC 255 Show that you can discuss the human reproductive system. III

SC 260 Given the continuation of the expansion of cities and the destruction of natural life, show that you can reasonably predict the change that will be apparent in the total environment. Report evidence to support your predictions. III

SECONDARY: BIOLOGY

(Life Science at the Secondary level is designated as Biology.)

SC 500 Show that you can use library resources to write a report on the distribution and characteristics of the subspecies of some animal (such as a squirrel), or plant (such as knotweed), in the United States. Suggest a hypothesis that would explain your findings. (A hypothesis is an idea stated in a way that it can be tested.) III

TERMINAL OBJECTIVES

SC 505 Demonstrate your ability to combine concepts, principles, and generalizations by designing an experiment involving an aquarium to show the effect of changes in temperature, light energy, dissolved gases, producers and consumers on a living community. V

SC 510 Demonstrate your ability to combine concepts, principles, and generalizations by designing a procedure for studying the biotic forms in a pond or lake in your community. Complete the study and discuss the nature of the relationships among the life forms you observed and their relationships to their environment. V

SC 515 Show your understanding of a taxonomic key by using the key to classify three given animals and three given plants. Describe each step you used, and end with the scientific name of each animal. III

SC 520 Show that you can classify living and non-living matter according to a taxonomic system. III

SC 525 Using a specific plant and animal, describe the mechanisms by which each life obtains and produces energy and synthesizes organic compounds. II

SC 530 Show that you can use specific examples drawn from the plant and animal kingdom to show your understanding of ways the differences in the mechanisms of mitosis and meiosis affect the nature of the offspring that result from asexual or sexual reproduction. III

SC 535 Demonstrate your ability to combine concepts, principles, and generalizations by designing an experiment using fruit flies to illustrate Mendel's laws. Complete each of the stages of the experiment and evaluate your results. V

SC 540 Using an example of a vascular plant and a non-vascular plant, show that you can write a description of the fate of nutrients taken into the plant and production of waste products by the plant. The structure in which each process takes place must be identified. III

TERMINAL OBJECTIVES

SC 545 Show your understanding of adaptations of muscular and skeletal systems of three selected vertebrates and three selected invertebrates that aid each organism in the process of obtaining food. II

SC 550 Show that you can reasonably predict the fate of a mammalian embryo and the embryo of one other animal if mechanisms for protection and nourishment should break down during the vulnerable embryonic and pre-embryonic period of their development. III

SC 555 Show that you can relate different characteristics of microorganisms such as *Euglena* and *Chlamydomonas* to those of viruses in one case and true plants and animals in another case. III

SC 560 Show that you can discuss factors that would make a microorganism infectious or non-infectious to a particular host on the basis of your knowledge of the effect of environmental factors on the growth of microorganisms. III

SC 565 Demonstrate your ability to combine concepts, principles, and generalizations about growth, production of energy, and elimination of waste products through the coordinated action of the digestive, respiratory, circulatory, and excretory systems by designing a schematic representation showing how food consumed by man is used. V

SC 570 Demonstrate your ability to perceive the relationship of the behavior of a person who is threatened and then struck by an object and the resultant behavioral changes in the endocrine and nervous system. Emphasize the interrelatedness of the activities of these systems. IV

SC 575 Show that you can use correct terminology to describe learned and unlearned behavior of a group of animals selected by the teacher and observed for periods of time totaling several hours. III

SC 580 Demonstrate your ability to perceive relationships by drawing and analyzing your family tree or the family tree of an acquaintance. Attempt to explain the presence of

TERMINAL OBJECTIVES

three family traits according to Mendel's laws, and then according to present day knowledge of genetics, citing the scientist responsible for theories you use. IV

SC 585 Demonstrate your ability to perceive the effect of uncontrolled population growth by conducting an experiment involving small fish, such as guppies. Report your observations graphically, analyze your results, and speculate on the significance of this experiment in regard to uncontrolled human population growth. IV

SC 590 Make judgments involving the gains and losses derived by other living things resulting from three examples of man's ability to control his environment. Identify the enabling characteristic of man in each case. VI

SC 595 After you have made an ecological analysis of five taxonomically classified plants or animals, show your understanding of the values of the taxonomical system or the ecological system to the biologist. II

SC 600 Given a scientific question or problem involving biology, demonstrate your ability to combine concepts, principles, and generalizations by developing relevant hypotheses that could be tested through a series of experiments. V

PHYSICAL SCIENCE

PRIMARY

SC 030 Show that you know about simple machines by identifying them in groups of pictures or examples. I

SC 035 Show your understanding of objects by classifying them according to type, form, and properties. II

SC 040 Show your understanding of forms of energy. II

SC 045 Show your understanding of interactions in the physical world. II

TERMINAL OBJECTIVES

SC 050 Show your understanding of relationships of objects and interactions in systems. II

INTERMEDIATE

SC 265 Show your understanding of the relative positions of stationary and moving objects. II

SC 270 Demonstrate your ability to combine concepts, principles, and generalizations by designing three experiments that show (1) the increase or decrease of the speed of an object, and (2) velocity as a function of time. V

SC 275 Given a demonstration of a moving object, show that you can use these terms to explain the phenomena: *force, inertia, energy, work, friction.* III

SC 280 Given a description or a diagram, show your understanding of atoms, elements, molecules, compounds, and mixtures. II

SC 285 Show that you can construct a model of an element showing the relationship between the atomic number of the element and the number of electrons in an atom of the element. III

SC 290 Show that you can use water to demonstrate the three phases of matter. Explain the changes at the molecular level and describe the properties at each phase. III

SC 295 Show that you can demonstrate the effects of heat on matter. Describe the effects in terms of molecular change. III

SC 300 Show your understanding of physical and chemical properties and changes. II

SC 305 Demonstrate your ability to combine concepts, principles, and generalizations by designing an experiment that demonstrates three examples of chemical change and by explaining the chemical changes that take place. V

TERMINAL OBJECTIVES

SC 310 Show your understanding of an internal-combustion engine in terms of potential, kinetic, electrical, chemical, and mechanical energy. II

SC 315 Given a simple machine, show that you can demonstrate its mechanical advantages. III

SC 320 Demonstrate your ability to combine concepts, principles, and generalizations about Newton's basic laws by designing a simple experiment that illustrates their application. Develop a hypothesis, test it with variables, draw conclusions, and make generalizations. V

SC 330 Demonstrate your ability to combine concepts, principles, and generalizations by producing an electric motor or transformer, correctly wiring a model. Explain the model in terms of (1) watts, (2) voltage, (3) resistance, (4) kilowatt-hours, and (5) electron movement. V

SC 335 Show your understanding of relationships between mass, volume, and density. II

SC 340 Show that you can demonstrate the relationship between magnetic force and electricity. III

SC 345 Show that you can interpret diagrams that illustrate the principles of sound. III

SC 350 Demonstrate your ability to combine concepts, principles, and generalizations by designing and presenting a demonstration of the nature and behavior of light. V

SC 355 Show your understanding of the processes by which nuclear energy is produced. II

SC 360 Show that you can predict possible uses for computers. Explain your predictions in as much detail as possible. III

SECONDARY: CHEMISTRY

(Physical Science at the Secondary level is divided into Chemistry and Physics.)

TERMINAL OBJECTIVES

SC 605 Show that you can demonstrate the structure of matter (atoms, elements, compounds, isotopes, etc.) by drawing models. III

SC 610 Using the periodic table, show that you can reasonably predict the chemical and physical properties of three elements not previously discussed. Base your prediction on a knowledge of their atomic numbers. III

SC 620 Given ionic equations that represent the reactions of selected acids or bases, show that you can reasonably predict the properties of the substances and their reactions to different indicators. III

SC 625 Given a list of twelve elements containing both metals and nonmetals, show that you can reasonably predict which elements will form chemical bonds with one another and whether these compounds are ionic or covalent. Show that you can give the formula for the most common form of combination. III

SC 630 Demonstrate your ability to combine concepts, principles, and generalizations by designing an experiment that will demonstrate the differential behaviors of solutions having the same molar strength but containing either ionic or non-ionic solutes. V

SC 635 Demonstrate your ability to perceive the relationship of nuclear equations to the decay of two isotopes (such as 131_I and 32_p). Determine the relative number of particles emitted by each nucleus after a given time period. IV

SC 640 Show that you can write a paper describing how hydrocarbons may be processed in industry to yield products useful to modern man. III

SC 645 Given reactants and conditions for several organic reactions, show that you can reasonably predict the principal products and can identify these products by formula and name. III

SC 650 Knowing the value for K_A of an acid and its concentration in a solution, show your understanding of reaction by calculating the pH of the solution. II

TERMINAL OBJECTIVES

SC 655 From a description of the results of an experiment involving a chemical change in which one of the products is a gas, demonstrate your ability to perceive the data using chemical equations. Relate the predicted weight and volume of gas to the actual yield. IV

SC 660 Demonstrate your ability to combine concepts, principles, and generalizations by developing a scheme of analysis for identifying the composition of an unknown solution or solid. Use a variety of laboratory tests, flame tests, precipitation, borax bead test, blowpipe tests (cobalt nitrate tests), and paper chromatography. Identify the unknown. V

SC 665 Show that you can discuss how the chemical and physical characteristics of carbohydrates and lipids, proteins, and nucleic acids make them particularly well-suited as sources of energy, enzymes, and hereditary material in the living cell. III

SC 670 Show that you can design an experiment in which you have to demonstrate how different forms of energy (including heat energy) can be produced in a chemical reaction. VI

SC 675 Using the table of oxidation potentials, show that you can reasonably predict reaction of three pairs of substances with one another. Explain the bases for your predictions. III

SC 680 Show that you can reasonably predict how changes in (1) pressure, (2) temperature, (3) concentration of reactants, and (4) addition of a catalyst, would affect the rate of a reaction and the point of equilibrium for that reaction. III

SC 685 Show your understanding of relationships of properties of colloidal particles to properties of macro-molecules such as proteins that are of colloidal size. II

SC 690 Demonstrate your ability to perceive energy changes associated with chemical reactions and physical changes. IV

TERMINAL OBJECTIVES

SC 695 Show that you can discuss the gas laws in terms of the amount of kinetic energy possessed by the molecules of gaseous substances. III

SC 700 Demonstrate your ability to combine principles, concepts, and generalizations by designing and performing an experiment concerning a problem in chemistry that you have defined. Write a complete laboratory report. V

SECONDARY: PHYSICS

SC 705 Given a brief history of the development of a physical law, show your understanding of the law's history by indicating the period of time when the law was first a hypothesis, when the hypothesis became a theory, and when the theory became a law. II

SC 710 Show that you can make measurements and calculations with respect to time, distance, area, and volume as required in word problems and express results in scientific notation. III

SC 715 Demonstrate your ability to combine concepts, principles, and generalizations by developing mathematical functions to express relationships in physics and applying the equations in solving word problems. V

SC 720 Demonstrate your ability to combine concepts, principles, and generalizations by developing relationships among the various properties of objects moving in space. V

SC 725 Show that you can demonstrate the properties of forces and the ways in which properties interact. III

SC 730 Demonstrate your ability to perceive relationships expressed in the conservation laws and to solve problems utilizing these laws. IV

SC 735 Demonstrate your ability to perceive relationships expressed in the kinetic theory of gases and to solve problems utilizing this theory. IV

TERMINAL OBJECTIVES

SC 740 Show that you can demonstrate the characteristics of wave motion. III

SC 745 Make judgments involving the characteristics of light waves. VI

SC 750 Demonstrate your ability to perceive relationships among the principles of optics. IV

SC 755 Demonstrate your ability to perceive relationships expressed in the quantum theory of light by solving problems utilizing this theory. IV

SC 760 Demonstrate your ability to perceive electric charges and electric current and to analyze the relationships between them under various conditions. IV

SC 765 Demonstrate your ability to perceive relationships between magnetic fields and the currents producing them. IV

SC 770 Show your understanding of electromagnetic induction by demonstrating its principles. III

SC 775 Show that you can present the evidence for modern theories concerning particles of matter. III

SC 780 Demonstrate your ability to perceive relationships of evidence and experiments to the concepts of quantum systems and quantum mechanics. IV

SC 785 Show that you can write and present a paper on an area in which physics is currently being widely employed and in which its frontiers are being expanded. Include prospects for future development. III

earTH science

PRIMARY

SC 055 Show your understanding of the solar system in terms of rotation and revolution of the earth, and in terms of properties of the sun and earth. II

SC 060 Show your understanding of a diagram that illustrates the soil-making process. II

SC 065 Show your understanding of relationships of ideas and objects to prehistoric life. II

INTERMEDIATE

SC 365 Show your understanding of the observational data used by meteorologists in predicting weather. II

SECONDARY

SC 790 Show that you can discuss the relative positions of the various astronomical bodies in the universe. Describe the nature of forces among the astronomical bodies. III

SC 795 Show your understanding of the origin and nature of rocks of the earth. II

SC 800 Show your understanding of composition of the earth, conditions under which various materials were formed, and ways and means of testing the materials making up the earth. II

SC 805 Show that you can discuss how and why changes occur in the features of the earth. III

SC 810 Demonstrate your ability to perceive relationships of the various factors that create weather conditions. IV

SC 815 Show your understanding of the various ways in which water interacts with the land. II

TERMINAL OBJECTIVES

SC 820 Show your understanding of the nature of the sea-air interface. II

SC 825 Given a description of environments and using biome maps and climatogram information, demonstrate your ability to perceive the probably distribution of living things. IV

SC 830 Show that you can discuss a description of work done by a group of scientists on sediment dating and radioactive clock methods of dating. Consider how their results clarify the mechanisms involved in the decline of one group of animals and the increase in another group of animals. III

SC 835 Show that you can reasonably predict the success of various methods of preventing and controlling pollution. III

SCIENCE INQUIRY SKILLS

PRIMARY

SC 070 Demonstrate the ability to collect information, through reading and interviewing, about the interaction of organisms with their environment. III

SC 075 Demonstrate ability to keep records of observation, reading, and interviewing in the form of lists, notes, or pictures. III

SC 080 Demonstrate your ability to conduct a simple experiment, making observations, keeping records, and relating the results to a given hypothesis.

INTERMEDIATE

SC 370 Demonstrate your ability to combine concepts, principles, and generalizations by designing an experiment in which these principles of learning are demonstrated: (1) learned and unlearned behavior, (2) memorization, (3)

forgetting, and (4) relearning. Use the following procedures in the experiments. V
1. Formulate a hypothesis based on observations.
2. Organize your experiment with variables.
3. Draw conclusions and make generalizations.
4. Write a formal report of your findings.

SC 375 Demonstrate that you can combine concepts, principles, and generalizations by developing a plan for increasing your efficiency in achieving objectives through the use of effective study skills. V

SC 380 Show your understanding of information about individual differences by describing a given number of your classmates. II

SC 385 Show that you can use science equipment and supplies in the classroom including (1) simple microscope, (2) Bunsen burner, (3) chemicals, (4) test tubes and other glassware, (5) thermometers. III

SC 390 Show that you can design an experiment, formulate a hypothesis, record your procedures and observations, draw conclusions regarding the hypothesis, and report your results. III

SC 395 Show that you can use a taxonomic system in scientific classification. III

SC 400 Show that you can use scientific information to make a model or conduct an experiment that demonstrates a scientific principle. III

SECONDARY

SC 840 Show that you can use the metric system of measurement by applying the system in all scientific experiments performed during the year. III

SC 845 In the laboratory, show that you can use equipment by (1) correctly identifying and reproducing in a drawing three structures of microscopic size, and (2) using the gas burner and the filtering system properly. III

TERMINAL OBJECTIVES

SC 850 Demonstrate your ability to perceive relationships in a laboratory experiment by making inferences and predictions based upon quantitative results that you have tabulated and graphed. IV

SC 855 Demonstrate your ability to combine concepts, principles, and generalizations by designing and conducting an experiment to test the validity of a given hypothesis and by analyzing and reporting the results. V

SC 860 Show that you can make reasonable predictions based on laboratory observations and measurements stated in a table or in graph form, using either interpolation or extrapolation. (Interpolation: predicting between two points; extrapolation: predicting beyond the last known point.) III

INDEX

INDEX

INDEX

INDEX

INDEX

INDEX

INDEX

INDEX

INDEX

INDEX

INDEX

INDEX

INDEX

INDEX

INDEX

INDEX

INDEX

INDEX

INDEX

INDEX

INDEX

INDEX

INDEX

INDEX

INDEX

INDEX

Behavioral Objectives

A Guide to Individualizing Learning

Text: Videocomp 9 point Roma with 10 point Roma Bold, display lines in 14 point Dimensia
Design and art: Steven Jacobs Design, Palo Alto, California
Editorial and production: Westinghouse Learning Press, Palo Alto, California
Composition, lithography, binding, packaging: Kingsport Press, Kingsport, Tennessee